SHARK
ATTACK!

SHARK ATTACK!

The Dangers Lurking in Australian Waters

Mike Edmonds

The Five Mile Press

The Five Mile Press

The Five Mile Press Pty Ltd
950 Stud Road
Rowville Victoria 3178 Australia

Phone:+61 3 8756 5500
Fax: +61 3 8756 5588
Email: publishing@fivemile.com.au

First published in 2003.
Text copyright © Mike Edmonds and individual copyright-holders
All rights reserved.

Cover design by Aimee Forde
Designed by SBR Productions Olinda Victoria
Edited by E Borghesi
Printed in Australia by Griffin Press

National Library of Australia Cataloguing-in-Publication data

Edmonds, Mike.
Shark attack!: dangers lurking in Australian waters

ISBN 1 86503 887 3

1. Shark attacks – Australia. 2. Sharks – Australia.
3. Shark attacks – Australia – Prevention. I. Title

597.340994

About the Author

As a journalist and fisherman, Mike Edmonds has come across sharks in various forms and various places in over three decades of covering the news and holding a fishing rod. As a journalist, he has written about shark attacks on other people, and as a fisherman he has caught a few (only small ones so far), and watched many others from the sometimes flimsy safety of a small boat.

He has a love-hate relationship with sharks. 'They are great sport and some make very good eating, but while you are out in the ocean the scales are finely balanced. It's their world, and they might just wind up hunting you.' It is this sort of relationship that has seen Mike develop a long-term fascination and respect for sharks.

Mike lives in Melbourne with his wife and has three children and two grandchildren. He doesn't care much for birthdays, but was 53 at last count. He loves a good feed of freshly caught fish, and when not working he is likely to be found on a lonely stretch of surf beach early in the morning or late evening – because even if the fish aren't on, the sunrises and sunsets make it all worthwhile.

Contents

Two Hundred Years of Shark Attacks

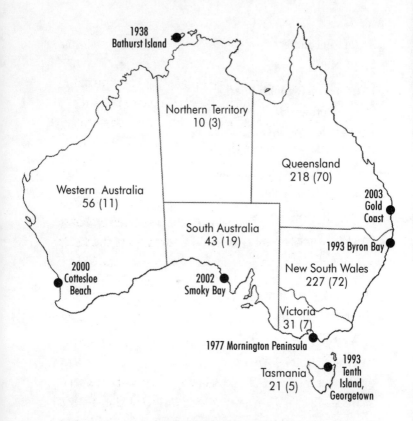

1938
Bathurst Island

Northern Territory
10 (3)

Queensland
218 (70)

2003
Gold
Coast

Western Australia
56 (11)

South Australia
43 (19)

1993 Byron Bay

New South Wales
227 (72)

2000
Cottesloe
Beach

2002
Smoky Bay

Victoria
31 (7)

1977 Mornington Peninsula

Tasmania
21 (5)

1993
Tenth
Island,
Georgetown

Shark death statistics:
1803–2003

The figures on this map show the number of recorded attacks
for each state, with fatal attacks in brackets. The date and
location of the most recent recorded attacks in each state or
territory is also noted. (These statistics were compiled in
February 2003.)

Introduction

*I*t may seem that over the past decade or so the number of shark attacks in Australia has been rising steadily. There's no scientific evidence to back up this belief. Some years are statistically worse than others, but then there are years when incidents, attacks and sightings are well down on the average.

The feeling that more sharks are out there just waiting for a hapless human to blunder into their jaws can probably be put down to a greater national awareness of sharks. It can also be sheeted home to the fact that coastal living, whether permanently or just the holiday shack, has jumped several rungs in the national desirability stakes.

All around the coast more people are getting involved in water sports, which means more people are venturing into the shark habitat.

The advent of cheap and reliable powerboats has seen fishing go through a recreational boom period. Sail-boards often outnumber yachts on the water on a fine spring or summer's day, surfing is no longer restricted to the dedicated few with their heavy and bulky three-metre plus Malibu long-boards, and personal watercraft, or jet-skis as they are commonly known, make it easy for people to get out where the big fish live.

While southern Australian waters appear to have the greatest numbers of great white sharks, it seems Sydney Harbour and the Western Australian coastline have the greatest number of non-fatal incidents.

Of course, Sydney Harbour and many Queensland beaches have long been the scene of anti-shark measures. The netting of Sydney's favourite beaches to separate swimmers from sharks is a process which started decades ago. This can be put down again to population pressures.

The Great Australian Bight is a world-renowned deep-water fishing ground, full of seal colonies and any self respecting great white would see it as an upper-class place to live and hunt. It is also relatively under-populated, unlike the waters of Sydney Harbour, where any shark showing a trace of dorsal fin is likely to be spotted.

But the southern and south-western coastline of Western Australia, while there is more shallow water, has uninterrupted access for the hunters of the deep from anywhere in the Indian Ocean. Despite being fairly common sharks have only launched 11 documented fatal attacks in waters all along the Western Australian coast since 1803, and only two of those have been at metropolitan Perth beaches.

The ocean is not a natural habitat for human beings. We can splash around on top quite happily, blissfully unaware of what could be going on below. But any further ventures require mechanical aids – such as a lump of shaped Styrofoam covered in fibreglass which allows us to ride the waves. Add a boom and a sail and it's a sailboard. Or we could use a basically simple Self Contained

Underwater Breathing Apparatus – SCUBA – to allow us to breathe for a fairly short time below the surface. On the other hand it could be a much more complex watercraft, ranging from the humble tinny to the largest ocean liner, allowing us to cover long distances and keep our feet dry. But these are all mechanical aids.

Without them we are restricted to the top few metres of a mysterious world. The intricacies of exactly how the world works beneath the surface of the ocean are still largely unknown. What we do know though, is there are dangers down there. And one of the most potent, which engenders a primeval fear in the human psyche, is the shark.

On current evidence, they've been around for approximately 400 million years. They were swimming the oceans of a still developing world long before the dinosaur's brief rule on land. And recent discoveries indicate that some of them back then were monsters in their own right, far bigger than the enormous but relatively benign whale shark, the giant of today's known species. And meaner. They had the size of a bus and the temperament of a rogue elephant.

Evolution has seen an end to those particular giants, but there are still plenty of other sharks around. Something in excess of 300 species of shark have been categorized in today's oceans. The number is a little rubbery, because new species are being discovered reasonably regularly. Fortunately, only a few of the known species are considered dangerous to humans.

Experts are very fond of telling us we have more chance of meeting our end by drowning in the ocean rather than as a meal for a passing pelagic. In fact, they constantly tell us the drive to the beach presents more of a risk than any shark.

Why then, does the blood run cold and some deep-seated fear-response set in when the cry of 'Shark!' goes up among a crowd of sun-loving, carefree beach-goers?

Why does a shark attack guarantee the victim massive media coverage, especially if he or she survives and can talk about the terror of the ordeal?

Sharks, it seems, get an even worse press than crocodiles, yet the death toll from sharks in Australia is about one per year. Small cheese it would seem statistically, but big news.

This book is by no means definitive. It does not cover every shark attack that has ever occurred in Australian waters; that would be an impossible mission.

In any event there have undoubtedly been more shark-related fatalities than the statistics indicate. A proportion of people who are listed as lost at sea or presumed drowned will have been the victims of a hungry great white or bronze whaler. Some fishermen who just never returned home will also have fallen prey to a passing shark.

In many cases, even if human remains are found and test positive to shark attack, the victim was often alone, in an isolated area of the coast or diving well out to sea near some little known reef. There was no-one around to see, and later recall, exactly what happened.

But the events recounted here all have their own levels of terror. Some are tales of incredible bravery, some of incredible stupidity. Not all resulted in death and some not even in disfigurement. But all are fascinating aspects of the interaction between sharks and us humans who think we rule the whole planet.

Finally, try some of the recipes at the end of this book. It's a most satisfying way of getting back at sharks.

Mike Edmonds
Melbourne 2003

Sharks in Our Waters

Sharks Around Australia

When marine biologists get together and throw a few nice fillets of flake and some prawns on the barbie, the talk naturally swings towards sharks. But for scientific purposes sharks, sawfish, stingrays and chimaeras (also called ghostfish) are all lumped in together. Way, way back it seems they all had a common ancestor (the fish that is, not the scientists). Over time, they went their different ways and developed their own distinct characteristics, although some species of sharks can still be confused with stingrays and vice versa, and you could be forgiven for mistaking a sawfish dorsal fin breaking the surface of the water for a shark fin. In any event, it's probably time to get out of the water …

Some even confuse professional fishermen. For instance, the shark ray, which is sometimes caught in waters stretching from Queensland's south coast across the top of the continent, and also south to about halfway down the Western Australian coast. It grows to about 2.7 metres long, and has two distinct shark-like dorsal fins along with the flattened head of a stingray. Even its name gives it a fin in both camps and, just to add a bit more room for error into the mix, it's also known as the mud skate or the bowmouth guitarfish. But the common characteristic appears to be the lack of a skeleton as we know a skeleton; that is, a bunch of separate bones, all interconnected – just like the old song says about the thigh-bone being connected to the hip-bone.

Sharks and their relatives don't have a bony skeleton holding all the bits together; instead, evolution came up with a cartilage structure, far softer than bones and very flexible, to keep everything in place (see page 219). Overall, there are more than 300 known species of sharks, rays (which includes skate), sawfish and chimaeras in Australian waters.

But of the sharks, only five types have been definitely identified as launching unprovoked attacks on humans, and five others are regarded as potentially dangerous. White pointers, tiger sharks, bull sharks, bronze whaler sharks and oceanic whitetip sharks are the known villains. The hammerhead, the blue shark, the mako, the grey nurse and the cutely named wobbegong (harmless by name but not by nature) are all suspected of not being averse to a bit of human entrée.

Convicted

The White Pointer

This is the one they make movies about. Officially, and very plainly, it is simply called the white shark, but Australians know better that it's anything but a plain ordinary shark. So it's labelled the great white shark, the white pointer, or white death, and sits right at the very top of the underwater food chain. Named for its generally white underbelly colour, the white shark can grow to six metres – considerably longer than most recreational fishing boats. Even then, it is not the biggest shark in Australian waters, only the most dangerous.

To compare its size with other sharks, the giant basking shark can grow to ten metres, while the whale shark is the grand-daddy of them all, reaching a whopping 12 metres (longer than the average in-ground backyard pool). Fortunately, both are quite sedate and don't have the teeth to match that of the great white, and feed on much smaller sea creatures by filtering vast quantities of water through their mouths, a little like live trawl nets. In contrast, the teeth on a great white are triangular, serrated on the edges and purpose-built to chomp hard and often.

The great whites live mainly in continental shelf waters, generally around the southern half of Australia, but are most common in the Great Australian Bight and around Tasmania. They have been declared a protected species, but if you want to get an idea of what it would be like to look one in the eye, there are a few displays around the country with preserved or frozen examples, and a number of life-size models at a few other marine display centres.

The foremost expert on white pointers in the country is Rodney Fox, still called the 'miracle man' after surviving a great white attack. He was all but bitten in half and certainly should have become a statistic on the fatality side of the ledger, but somehow lived to tell the tale. (See page 102 for Rodney's story.)

Researchers have pretty much agreed now that a great white, in fact any shark, will take a test bite of potential food before deciding whether to go ahead with its meal. This is regarded as what saved Rodney Fox – the beast who attacked him simply didn't like the taste. Experiments with a surfboard also appeared to confirm anecdotal evidence that sharks take a 'test bite'.

'Rodney Fox may have survived because the shark took a test bite and didn't like the taste of him,' according to

Professor Ross Miller, from the University of Adelaide. But the power and strength of the white death is such that even a test bite will more than likely prove fatal.

Research by Professor Miller and his associate, research engineer John Watkins, on great whites in the Neptune Islands group, south of Port Lincoln, found that, in terms of 'sheer chomping power', the force exerted by a 3.2-metre shark biting with its entire jaws would be equivalent to the weight of 1.5 tonnes. Their detailed work found a 3.2-metre white shark would be capable of lifting an average-sized car with its jaw muscles. They also found the force exerted by a similar-sized shark making off with prey was roughly equivalent to four or five men pulling with all their strength in a tug-of-war.

After finalising results, Mr Watkins said: 'You'd have no chance of resisting an attack.' Details of the research by Professor Miller and Mr Watkins have been published in *Adelaidean*, the university's newspaper.

The research team set out to obtain shark bite impressions on a variety of materials used in aquatic equipment and to make measurements of bite force and the speed and force at which sharks take and make off with prey. Such research is vital for designing shark-proof equipment.

Speed tests on the great whites indicated an average cruising speed of about three kilometers per hour with short bursts of up to 16 kilometres per hour. Professor Miller says that, to put this in perspective, Australia's Olympic gold medallist, Kieran Perkins, swam at about 6.5 kilometres per hour in the 1,500-metre event. And the research also found that great whites liked hats. Mr Watkins had his brand new hat blown off by the wind during research – only to watch it land in the water and be swallowed by a 'monster of the deep'.

The Tiger Shark

The tiger shark is actually a fairly friendly-looking fellow – but then so was Ned Kelly, so don't be fooled. There are very good reasons for the tiger shark being named the way it is, and not all of them are to do with its appearance.

Known only as the tiger shark, there's no need for any other name. And, just as with their land-based namesakes, don't even think about making friends with one. They're a big beast when fully grown, right up there with the great white shark at six metres or so, although at birth they only measure about 50 centimetres. So, if you happen to come across one, have a quick pray that it's a baby, and that mum or dad aren't hanging around.

The tiger shark is so-named because at birth the young have a very distinct series of dark stripes on their upper surfaces, but by the time they reach half their full size, the stripes have faded and merged. The teeth are also distinctive, shaped something like a rooster's comb and serrated on both edges like your average breadknife – designed, in fact, not to let go once they get a grip on whatever tasty morsel takes their fancy. These fellows are quite common in Australia's tropical waters, but during summer they can get down to the southern New South Wales and Western Australian coastal regions if the water is warm enough.

Bronze Whaler

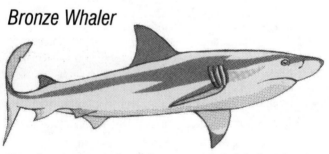

Now here's a member of an extended family. The term 'whaler shark' is a catchall term for several types of shark, most (but not all) of which are in the genus *Carcharhinus*. Some are dangerous, and some are not, and the frequent use of the term 'whaler' can therefore be very confusing and misleading. The bronze whaler, however, has the official name of *Carcharhinus brachyurus*, and has been involved in various fatal shark-related incidents in Australian waters.

The bronze is found in waters right around the mainland and Tasmanian coasts, and is a specific target of commercial fishers in Western Australia. In the west, the gill net boats are usually after young fish, anything from 70 centimetres upwards, but bronzes also fall victim to the long-line boats. It has a brown to grey body colour, with an obvious bronze sheen (although some other sharks also display a bronze glow, especially in sunlight).

The bronze whaler when fully grown can get close to four metres long – not the sort of thing you want to share a wave with.

Bull Shark

The bull shark, like the bronze whaler, is a member of the *Carcharhinus* genus (its official name is *Carcharhinus leucas*) and is in fact often confused with the bronze whaler. The bull shark is sometimes referred to as a 'river shark', presumably because it is often found in murky or muddy water and likes to breed in the mouth of rivers. It is an aggressive and opportunistic feeder, and has been implicated most often in shark attacks around the world. It is a heavy-bodied shark with broad, serrated triangular upper teeth. It is believed that it lives to about 14 years, and grows to approximately 3.5 metres in length.

Oceanic Whitetip

This shark is also a member of the *Carcharhinus* genus, and so is commonly referred to as being one of the many kinds of whaler sharks. The oceanic whitetip spreads itself around most of the coast and, as the name implies, well into the open ocean waters from the south-west coast of Western Australia, across the Northern Territory and north Queensland coasts and down to just north of Sydney. Strangely enough, whitetips tend to keep out of the Gulf of Carpentaria, perhaps because the water is shallower than they prefer, and generally out of southern waters because the water is too cold. One whitetip, however, presumably lost, has been taken off Port Lincoln on the Great Australian Bight.

The whitetip gets its name from the mottled white tips which decorate the dorsal, tail and pectoral fins, and the dorsal and pectoral fins themselves are also a giveaway. The tips are rounded, rather than the traditional image of a sharply pointed shark fin.

Suspected

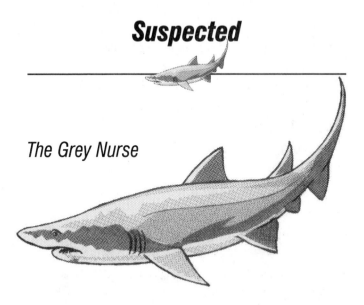

The Grey Nurse

Now here's an ugly customer, sometimes likened to mothers-in-law in places where blokes talk to other blokes and no women – especially wives – are around. Unlike mothers-in-law, the grey nurse is protected in Australian waters. They're a good deal stouter than many other sharks, but still streamlined and still efficient predators, with long rather than triangular teeth. They grow to a bit over three metres long and have been found in waters around the entire Australian coast, although it has been many years since a grey nurse has been spotted in southern Australian waters. The grey nurse is also known as the sand tiger shark and the spotted ragged tooth, and its most recognizable feature is the two large dorsal fins of almost the same size.

Overseas studies have found the grey nurse to be migratory, shifting from place to place in a definite pattern, repeated over the years. This is assumed to be linked to its reproductive cycle, but no studies have been carried out on grey nurses in Australian waters.

The Hammerhead

There are two types of hammerhead sharks in Australian waters, the smooth and the scalloped (pictured). The major difference is that the scalloped hammerhead has an indentation in the middle of the front edge of its distinctively broad, flattened head. Both are known simply as hammerheads, and since it's such a perfect description, no other colloquial names have come into use.

The smooth hammerhead is found in southern Australian waters, including Tasmania, and up to about halfway along the east and west coasts. The scalloped hammerhead is found in northern waters and down the west coast to as far as Bunbury and the east coast to the Merimbula region. Both are targeted by professional fishermen, with fins and carcasses being used, and both grow to about 3.5 metres.

The Blue

This baby is found all around Australia and Tasmania except in the Gulf of Carpentaria, the Arafura Sea and Torres Strait. Blue sharks are also sometimes known as blue whalers (apparently because of their taste for whale flesh). They are very slim, especially compared to other sharks like the grey nurse, and easily distinguished because of the bright blue upper body colour, long, pointed snout and very long pectoral fins.

Blue sharks have a mouthful of nice sharp triangular teeth. They have been recorded as being up to 3.8 metres long, but are more commonly 2–2.5 metres. They are the tourists of the shark world, ranging far and wide, and have been known to cross oceans from one side to the other.

The Shortfin Mako

The shortfin mako covers much of the same territory as the blue shark and has similar, but not quite as distinctive, colouring. It's also known as the blue pointer, mackerel shark, mako shark and snapper shark. The shortfin mako is sometimes confused with the blue shark, but instead of the blue's triangular teeth, it has long, slender, smooth-edged choppers and the upper and lower sections of the caudal (tail) fins are roughly the same size.

The shortfin mako is regarded as a commercial fish, with fins and flesh finding their way to market. They grow to almost four metres. There is also a longfin mako, but the shortfin is much more common.

The Wobbegong

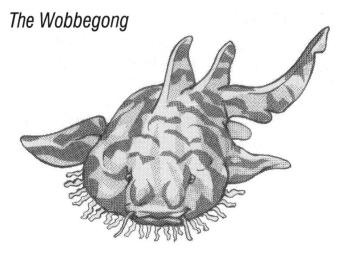

Despite the cute name, which makes it sound like something from a children's storybook, this ugly beast does have teeth, and will use them. It lives on the seabed, partially burying itself as it waits for prey to swim within reach, and the surest way to upset one is to accidentally step on it. It's sort of at the halfway mark between a shark and a stingray, with a flattened head and body and elongated tail. There are a few varieties of wobbegongs in Australian waters, all coloured to blend into the seabed.

The tasselled wobbegong (pictured) can be found in coastal waters north of the Tropic of Capricorn, and is common in shallow inshore waters and around offshore reefs. It has a distinctive mosaic skin pattern, and a heavy fringe of fleshy tassels around the mouth, which is at the front of the snout. The tasselled wobbegong is fairly small by shark standards, growing to a bit over one metre.

The other major member of the family is the banded wobbegong, found in waters stretching south from the tip of Cape York in Queensland, right around the coast to the Geraldton region in Western Australia. It stays mostly in southern waters, however, and lacks the complex mosaic skin pattern of its northern cousin. It also lacks most of the fleshy tassels around the mouth, but what it lacks in looks it makes up for in size, growing to about three metres.

(Illustrations reproduced courtesy Lee Krutop)

Fatal Attacks

The Attacks Of 2000:
Annus Horribilus

*T*he end of the year 2000 was the signal for a world party and to hell with the mathematicians and theorists who proved time after time it wasn't really the end of a millennium. It was also an absolute shocker year for shark attacks in Australia.

Since 1958, the University of Florida has kept a data base of unprovoked shark attacks around the world, and 2000 saw 79 attacks recorded, the highest annual tally in more than four decades of record-keeping. Ten of the attacks resulted in loss of life. Australia, with seven attacks, was second on the ladder for total attack numbers, well behind the United States, where 51 attacks were recorded for the year. But Australian beaches led the world in fatal attacks. Of the seven recorded incidents in Australian waters that year, three were fatal. Despite the far higher number of attacks, only one fatality happened in the US. Australia's only challenger that year for fatal attacks was Tanzania, which had two deaths, and there was one each in Fiji, New Caledonia, Japan, Papua New Guinea, and as already mentioned, the US.

Two of the fatal Australian attacks took place within a 30-hour period on the South Australian coast and the third was in waist-deep water off a very popular near-city Perth beach. All three took place within a six-week period, and the Australian media went into a feeding frenzy worthy of a whole school of sharks.

The First Victim: Cameron Bayes

The first victim Cameron Bayes, 25, a New Zealander who was spending time travelling around Australia on a combined working holiday and honeymoon with his wife of seven months. The couple had been camping at Cactus Beach near Penong on the Eyre Highway, the road which stretches almost 1,700 kilometres across the Nullarbor Plain from near Port Augusta at the northern end of South Australia's Spencer Gulf to Norseman, 200 kilometres south of Kalgoorlie in Western Australia.

Cameron and his wife, Tina, were to have left Cactus Beach within days. They planned to keep ambling west, where Cameron was to have replenished their funds with some shearing work. However, a fine Sunday morning and some very good waves persuaded him to leave the campground for the renowned Cactus Beach surf. He was about 200 metres offshore at 7.30am on 24 September 2000 when the great white struck. It was between four and five metres long and made several rushes at its prey over 90 seconds that seemed to stretch for 90 minutes.

Jeff Hunter of Port Lincoln was also on the beach that morning enjoying another day of a family camping holiday with his two children. The way he described the attack fits precisely the style of the great white. A rush from below with deadly determination and a huge swirling in water that for a few moments turns blood red. Mr Hunter said afterwards there was no warning, and the shark just came straight in and attacked, thrashing around in a circular motion around Cameron.

'He seemed to get back on his board and was paddling back and it came in again,' he told the media afterwards. 'It was just horrendous – it totally took him out. It just seemed to roll on its belly then it thrashed around a bit more then it seemed to release the surfboard ... but there was nothing left of the guy.'

The final 30 or 40 seconds of the attack were witnessed by Peter Ryan, of Moana Beach, who walked over a sand dune and into a horror story.

'The thing really wanted him and it wasn't going to let him go,' he said later that Sunday. 'I just saw a flash of red as the wave came over and then it was all over. We saw the last 30 seconds and that took forever ... we were in disbelief that it could be that close.'

Mr Ryan described the killer as swimming around Cameron and creating a whirlpool which dragged him down. That may well be how it appeared to him, looking down on the water from the top of a sand dune, but it is far more likely the shark was just making repeated passes at its target, sometimes finding flesh and blood and sometimes the surfboard in its mouth. Cameron's surfboard was recovered afterwards in several pieces, and the remains bore obvious evidence of the attack.

Tina Bayes, relaxing back at the campsite, had no idea of the ghastly fate her husband had met. When she was told by other surfers she immediately went into deep shock, and was cared for by other women in the campground until an ambulance arrived from Ceduna. She left Ceduna for New Zealand the day afterwards, a widow.[1] But a mere 30 hours after Cameron Bayes died, another surfer was to be taken by a white pointer only 250 kilometres away ...

The Second Victim: Jevan Wright

Jevan Wright was only 17 and was looking forward to his 18th birthday in a fortnight's time. He travelled from Port Lincoln, on the tip of the Eyre Peninsula, to Elliston, where he used to live, to visit his girlfriend and have a surf. He and his younger brother, Rhys, arrived at Elliston on the very day Cameron Bayes's life ended. Jevan had been working for almost 12 months on a Port Lincoln-based tuna fishing boat, and was within four weeks of finishing his traineeship. The tuna boat had just finished a trip, and consigned a large haul of fish to Japan, so the crew was given a well-earned ten-day lay-off.

The morning after the group reached Elliston, while the search was still underway for the body of Cameron Bayes 250 kilometres away, Jevan, a friend from interstate with whom he was travelling, and his girlfriend's father went to Blackfellas Point, just north of Elliston, for a surf. Early in the afternoon, just before 1pm on Monday 25 September 2000, they were all in the water seeking every surfer's dream – the perfect wave.

---

1. The death of Cameron Bayes was not the first at Cactus Beach. Twenty-five years earlier, in 1975, a 12-year-old boy, Wade Shippard, was taken by a white pointer while swimming at Point Sinclair at the eastern end of the beach.

Jevan was paddling towards shore 50–100 metres in front of his two companions when there was a thrashing in the water around his board. His companions said the water turned white, and then they saw a large tail fin break the surface and Jevan just disappeared. The only sign he had ever been in the water was the mangled remains of his surfboard. His surfing buddies got ashore as quickly as they could to raise the alarm and within half an hour local fishermen were searching the beach at Blackfellas. They were soon joined by police, State Emergency Service teams and other volunteers, but the shattered surfboard was all that was found.

The owner of the Elliston Caravan Park, Chris Marston, said later that sharks were not the only danger at Blackfellas. He said the waves were regarded as among the best in Australia, and attracted surfers from all over the country and from overseas. But there were a lot of reefs and unpredictable currents which made it more suited to skilled surfers than beginners. He said sharks were only occasionally reported in the area, and when they were reported they were usually put down as bronze whalers, regarded as less dangerous than the great whites. However, he said not all shark sightings were reported by the surfing fraternity for fear local authorities would close the beach.

Jevan's parents, Jeff and Katrina Wright, both keen surfers themselves, were at home when they got word of the tragedy from their younger son, Rhys. A close friend immediately drove them to Elliston, but there was nothing to be done except gather a few close friends together that night for a memorial service.

Two days after the attack, Jeff Wright told reporters he did not blame the shark which took their son. 'We're in their world ... you take your chances when you go out,' he said. 'It consoles me that he didn't know a thing when the attack happened.'

Mr and Mrs Wrights' main regret was that they were at a friend's house in Port Lincoln for a barbecue when the boys left to go surfing, and they were not able to say goodbye to them.

The deaths of Jevan and Cameron were 'sadly a case of tragic coincidence', said Barry Bruce, a scientist at the Commonwealth Scientific and Industrial Research Organisation (CSIRO) Marine Research Centre in Hobart, but added the incidents were 'too far apart to be the same shark'. Great whites do, however, cover more territory than it was thought only a few years ago, but the distance between the Wright and Bayes attacks (about 250 kilometres) seems too far for a shark to travel in just over a day.

A little over three weeks after the death of their son, the Wrights again travelled along the coast, but this time went past Elliston, where they lost Jevan, and continued on the Eyre Highway to Cactus Beach. There they joined the parents of Cameron Bayes, who had travelled from New Zealand to see the spot where their son had died. Cameron's sisters, Melanie and Katy, were also there, and the families, supported by locals and other surfers, threw roses into the water.

Mr Bayes told mourners that Cameron's wife, Tina, was too grief-stricken to return to the place she had last seen her husband. 'For her it is too soon to come back, but we hope this will help us to cope as a family,' he told the 70 people who had gathered on Cactus Beach. 'We had to come here as a family to make this terrible loss seem real.'

The Third Victim: Ken Crew

Tragically, within just three weeks of the memorial service at Cactus Beach, yet another family and community loss in Perth would become only too real. Ken Crew, 49, swam every day with a group of other middle-aged, mostly affluent, men from Perth's better-off suburbs. The group was known locally as 'The Pod', the collective term for a school of whales or seals, and their nickname was to prove tragically accurate.

On Monday 6 November 2000, as people around the world were planning massive end-of-millennium celebrations, Mr Crew, who owned a car-servicing business, joined his regular swimming partner, Fremantle lawyer Dirk Avery. It was just after 6am when they jogged into the water at North Cottesloe Beach, hesitating momentarily when Mr Crew asked: 'Is there something out there?' They decided it was probably just a seal, and continued to walk through the small Indian Ocean breakers.

As they reached waist-deep water, a five-metre white pointer arrowed in. The shark savaged Mr Crew's legs and dragged him under the water, but left him floundering, blood pouring from his wounds, and turned to attack 52-year-old Dirk Avery. Mr Avery thumped the water with his fists in an effort to drive the monster off, and the dreaded cry of 'Shark attack!' went up from the beach.

Kim Gamble at the time owned a café overlooking the beach, and was alerted by the cry. He said he walked onto the balcony of the Blue Duck Cafe, and could see the shark clearly. 'It was really huge,' he said later. 'There was a whole sea of blood and it was pulling the person.'

For some reason the shark did not press home its attack, and other swimmers were able to get the mortally wounded man onto a surf-ski, and back to the shore 40 metres away. Mr Avery had deep lacerations to his feet, but Ken Crew had lost one leg entirely, and the other was shredded.

Mr Crew's wife, Robin, was walking further along the beach when her husband was attacked. A friend told her what had happened and she rushed back along the sand as other swimmers made frantic attempts to slow the bleeding from her husband's horrific wounds. It was to no avail, and Ken Crew died on the sand with his wife by his side and a priest, Father Brian Morrison, who was also a member of The Pod, holding his hand and administering the last rites.

Minutes after he died a baby seal was seen frolicking in the surf not far from where Mr Crew was attacked. Western Australian Fisheries officers said the shark may actually have been lured inshore by the young seal, but spotted the members of The Pod and changed targets. They also said the killer was probably the same great white seen three times in the previous fortnight by fellow officers and fishermen as it patrolled along the Western Australian coastline. Dirk Avery was treated in hospital for his injuries, and allowed to leave later that same day.

The following morning, soon after dawn, Robin Crew and her three children, Aimee, 14, Andrew, 17, and Rebecca, 22, returned to Cottesloe Beach, where they were joined by Father Morrison and other members of The Pod, as well as dozens of other mourners. Father Morrison performed a simple service, and flowers were thrown into the crystal clear water, which 24 hours previously had briefly turned red with the blood of a dying man. He said afterwards it was a beautiful, gentle service.

'We spoke gently about Ken because we realized that we had built a deep, unspoken bond of friendship and this man was the pivot of that bond,' the priest said. 'At the last dying moment, I was holding his hand. I whispered in Kenny's ear and told him I was giving him the blessings of the church. He squeezed my hand.'

Despite being a protected species, the great white which killed Ken Crew was the subject of a one-off shoot-to-kill order signed by the then state Fisheries minister, Monty House. However the hunt was unsuccessful.

Almost two years later, Australian actor Heath Ledger pulled one of the most tasteless stunts ever seen on television. He was a guest on the nationally televised American late night talk show hosted by Jay Leno. Ledger joked about the attack, saying a 'paddler' had 'pissed off' the shark which 'bit him in half'. Ken Crew's widow, Robin, quickly heard about the joke, and was very upset. She told friends she thought Ledger's comments were in 'very poor taste'.

Ledger's Australian publicist, his sister, Kate, released

a statement from the actor, who said he was sorry. 'I wish to apologize to the family and friends of Ken Crew for any hurt or pain caused as a result of my recent conversation with Jay Leno on the *Tonight Show*,' the Ledger statement read. A fairly lame apology, was the general feeling, certainly in Perth.

At about the same time, arguments were still raging over safety at Cottesloe. Despite heavy pressure the beach, two years after Ken Crew was taken and five years after yet another incident when Brian Sierakowski and a mate were almost taken (see page 134), still did not have even the most basic of shark lookout towers for lifesavers to man. Swimmers, even the regulars, were nervous. Cottesloe, it seemed, had picked up a reputation as something of a jinxed beach. And while most people looked at the statistics and calculated the odds, they still had the savage death of Ken Crew at the back of their minds. Andrew Dimsey was swimming about 700 metres south of Ken Crew and the other members of The Pod when the shark struck. To this day he still considers himself lucky.

'It could have been me,' he said. 'It's like a [black] spot on the road; it makes you aware of what can happen.' Mr Dimsey kept swimming at Cottesloe, but he changed his routine. He never took to the water at dawn or dusk, on overcast days or during whale-migration periods, after the attack on Ken Crew. 'It is a warning that the ocean is not something to be taken lightly,' he said. 'Humans are just not very well-equipped in the water – certainly not as equipped as sharks are.'

Emma Lipscombe was also there that morning when

Mr Crew died. She was taking her regular walk along the sand. Two years later she vividly remembered seeing blood in the water. 'There was a tail thrashing back and forth and I did a double-take,' she said. 'I thought it must have been two sharks because one shark couldn't do that much damage and it was in such shallow water.' Her husband Tim, a keen surfer, arrived at the scene about half an hour later. Just a week before the attack, Emma had reluctantly agreed to a snorkelling trip with her daughter on the reef at Cottesloe. 'I was scared of sharks then,' she said. 'I wondered how I could let my children back in the water after this.'

The Cottesloe tragedy and near tragedies inspired Emma to learn what she could about sharks, for her own benefit and for the safety of her family, and to bring her fear into perspective. 'It is not fair to inflict that fear on our children,' she said. 'I've done a lot of reading and I have convinced myself that the shark came in for seals. It was early in the morning, it was grey and still, and I've read that a shark will corner a seal up against a reef in those conditions.' Like Mr Dimsey, Emma has returned to the ocean but she's much more careful now. 'Never at dawn or dusk, or when it's overcast,' she said.

A Cottesloe Attack in 1925

In November 1925, the beach was crowded with bathers when the cry of 'Shark!' went up. In the middle of a beautifully calm, warm afternoon hundreds of people scrambled from the water to the sand, only to turn back to the ocean in a bid to spot the beast which had panicked them. What they, and a group of lifesavers who were pushing a small surf-rescue boat into the water saw, was a surfer, face down in water which was turning a gruesome shade of red around his inert body. The victim, a bookies penciller, had been among a crowd of surfers enjoying the day at Cottesloe when he was, for some reason known only to the shark, singled out. As well as the rescue boat, three lifesavers had begun swimming from the safety of the beach towards the dying Samuel Ettleson as soon as he was spotted in the water. The swimmers and the boat crew reached him virtually simultaneously, but even as they were hauling him into the boat the killer shark made another rush.

Seeming to ignore the other people in the water, it arrowed straight for its original target, pushing the lifesavers aside like bits of kelp as it took another grab at his leg. One of the boat crew began belting the killer with a heavy wooden oar, forcing it to release Ettleson long enough for him to be hauled into the small craft, but the shark was not finished, even though its prey was no longer in the water. It swam off a short distance, then turned and rushed, torpedo-like, at the boat. The horrified watchers on the beach saw its huge head rear over the side of the boat as it slammed into the flimsy timbers, almost capsizing it. For the rest of the afternoon, long after Samuel Ettleson had been bought ashore and died despite medical treatment, the shark patrolled up and down Cottesloe Beach. It ignored the odd rifle shot fired at it as it cruised close to shore, and virtually nobody left the sand for as long as there was light to see by.

It was the chance of a lifetime to look, from safety, at a beast they had watched earlier display all the single minded tenacity of a determined killer.

The lone fatality in Fiji in that horror year 2000 also had a bizarre and grisly link with Australia. Michael Loxton, 47, an Australian who moved to Fiji in the early 1980s was attacked by a shark in shallow water off the Garden Island Resort. The shark bit his leg off, and he quickly bled to death even before he could be taken from the water. Michael was the son of Australian cricket legend, Sam Loxton, who, along with Sir Donald Bradman, Neil Harvey and Bill Brown, made up the backbone of the famed 1948 Invincibles team, which took the cricket world by storm.

Ray Boundy's Tale of Bravery – and Tragedy

*A*ny list of shark attacks in Australian waters must be incomplete. There are too many unexplained disappearances at sea, boats of all sizes sinking virtually without trace, surfers and fishers vanishing for no apparent reason. Some will have been taken by sharks, but nobody knows how many. Occasionally though, there are survivors who tell horrific stories of bravery and tragedy. Survivors who escape the jaws of death are able to recall the full horror of their experience years later, in full detail, every second indelibly imprinted in their memory. Ray Boundy, now nearing 50, lost two friends to the same shark 20 years ago, and was almost certainly about to become a third victim. He managed to scramble onto a reef and lived to tell a horrifying story which would otherwise have gone into the history books as another unexplained disappearance at sea.

About midnight on a Sunday night in July 1983, huge seas off Townsville overturned his fishing trawler, the *New Venture*. Boundy, his deckhand Dennis 'Smurf' Murphy, 24, and the *New Venture*'s cook, Murphy's 21-year-old girlfriend Lindy Horton, scrambled onto the wallowing hulk of the trawler, out of the water but not out of danger, as the swells washed over the slowly settling hull. For two hours the trio thanked their lucky stars they had at least survived the capsize. They had to abandon what little comfort the sinking boat offered and take to the water on a surfboard, a lifebuoy and one of the foam ice-boxes common on fishing boats for keeping the catch cool. All day Monday they floated, drifting further and further from the spot the *New Venture* capsized. They saw several sharks in the water but the undersea predators showed no interest, and the shipwrecked trio was able to keep their spirits up, confident rescue was only a matter of time.

A little after dusk on Monday, about 7.30pm, they drifted into the path of a five-metre tiger shark, which began circling the rag-tag collection of makeshift lifesaving devices. The shark left and the fear subsided a little. Soon afterwards, fear turned to horror as Ray Boundy felt a bite, or a scrape from the rough sandpaper-like skin of the shark, on his left knee. Instinctively he kicked out with his other leg, and the shark went away. Minutes later a wave knocked all three into the water and, as if it had been waiting for a signal, the shark returned. It grabbed Dennis Murphy by the leg, severing the limb and turning the water blood red as it swam away. Murphy, still alive but bleeding profusely, then shouted a warning to the others to swim away because the shark was coming back. He himself tried to move in the opposite direction, calling to Boundy to take care of Lindy when the shark moved in for the kill.

'Smurf kicked and punched and swore at the thing until it turned his body upside, lifting it high out of the water before diving with its tail thrashing,' Boundy told

Townsville *Bulletin* journalist Danny Mortison. It grabbed Murphy by the upper half of his body and dived under, mercifully stifling the doomed deckhand's screams, but leaving a mass of blood and flesh on the surface to be dispersed by the waves. Afterwards Boundy likened the experience to seeing his friend and shipmate fed through a mincer. He also now had sole responsibility for Lindy, who became hysterical with fear and shock after seeing her boyfriend eaten alive. Boundy had to slap her and shout abuse before she calmed down enough to concentrate again on survival. They stayed close in the water, Boundy holding onto Lindy's hand to keep her spirits up.

Fate played games with Ray Boundy that night. Eight hours later he was just beginning to think he and Lindy might make it to Lodestone Reef, but the monster returned and circled briefly before closing in.

'I saw the shark's eyes,' Boundy told the Brisbane *Sunday Mail* more than three years later. 'He turned on his side and lunged out of the water and grabbed Lindy from the life-ring by the arm and chest.

'It flung itself into the air and got the top half of her and turned her upside down. It was just so quick and she squealed and it shook her like a rag doll to get her out of the life-ring. She only let out one little squeal … I knew straight away she was dead.'

In sight of Lodestone Reef, Boundy thought the ordeal must surely be over. A few more hours of paddling and he would be out of the water. He was about 60 kilometres from where the *New Venture* went down, but well within the area of the search which must surely be under way by now. Then, as if to torment him beyond endurance, the shark returned, and began its ominous circling around and underneath him. It became a race, with life or death literally the prize. Ray Boundy paddled as fast as his depleted strength would allow, with the shark tracking him, and finally managed to catch a wave that took him to safety inside Lodestone reef, just as a search plane appeared overhead. The search aircraft whistled up a RAAF helicopter and soon Boundy was flying safely over the ocean, and the sharks which called it home, telling his rescuers through his exhaustion a story they could scarcely believe. To this day he believes without a shadow of doubt the same shark took two of his best friends, and was within seconds of taking him, despite a number of expert opinions which lean towards separate tiger or reef sharks taking Dennis Murphy and Lindy Horton as they trespassed in the shark's domain.

Terrors in Tasmanian Waters

*L*ike South Australia, Tasmania is renowned for its deep-water offshore fishing, and naturally where there are commercial quantities of fish there are other, larger, animals to eat the fish. All around the Tasmanian coast there are fish havens. There are rocky outcrops and reefs directly off the coast, as well as numerous reefs and islands jutting out of the water well away from the coastline itself and in Bass Strait. As the fish are attracted, so are the predators. Seal colonies abound because of the good food supplies for the adult seals and their young during the breeding season, and with the seals come their natural enemies – large and aggressive sharks. Some of these sharks are the dreaded white pointers, but tiger sharks and other confirmed man-eaters are also common.

In a little over the past 25 years there have been four fatal shark attacks in Tasmanian waters. Survivors have also told stories of horrifyingly close encounters with the monsters of the deep. Two of these stories, one of survival and one of death, are among the scariest shark tales to emerge from Australian waters, and there's a chance, slim according to some scientists but still a chance, the same shark was involved in both.

Shark Kills Quads' Mother

Therese Cartwright, mother of the Cartwright quads, then six years old, and a baby under one, was taken while diving off Weymouth on Tasmania's north-east coast. Her husband, Ian, the quads, Thomas, Sarah, James and Luke, and 11-month-old Paul, were with friends aboard a vessel operated by the Australian Maritime College. Ian was Director of the Fisheries and Environment Faculty at the college, and the Saturday, 5 June 1993, boating and diving trip was a pleasant way to combine a bit of work and a bit of recreation. Therese, a midwife, and another employee of the college, Stephen Earys, went diving near Tenth Island. Stephen entered the water first and swam to the bottom where he waited for his dive-buddy.

Therese followed, but stopped not far below the surface, apparently having trouble of some sort with her breathing gear. Nobody ever discovered what the fault was, because a massive white pointer charged from behind, launching just the one strike. It grabbed Therese in its gaping jaws and turned towards deep water, dragging the helpless woman with it. Within seconds the beast and its victim had totally vanished. A search started immediately, but nobody ever expected anything other than tragic confirmation of Therese Cartwright's death, and that very afternoon it was delivered. A search and rescue vessel from the Port of Launceston Authority recovered a human leg and a shredded and ripped piece of wetsuit, all that was ever found of Therese, despite boats scouring the ocean around the area for nearly a week afterwards.

The shark, in following its hunting and feeding instincts, had shattered the lives of an extraordinary family. Therese and Ian Cartwright met as children where they lived in an English seaside village. Therese was 19 when she married Ian and the couple moved to Tonga, where she quickly established herself as a caring and dependable nurse. In 1985 they moved to Tasmania, and their joint love of the sea was a major part of the decision to live in the West Tamar district. Therese returned to studying, and became the first nurse to graduate with distinction from the Launceston campus of the University of Tasmania. She continued studying and looking after her five children, working towards her Masters. The Cartwright family home was in Exeter, on the West Tamar Highway, which runs from the heart of Launceston northwards towards the coast on the western side of the gloriously wide Tamar River. Members of West Tamar Rotary, who six years earlier banded together to help the Cartwrights get organized when Therese came home from hospital with quads, got together once more, to help Ian Cartwright organize his future life without the quads' mother.

More than 12 months after the death of Therese Cartwright, a coroner put the final seal, at least legally, if not for the grieving family, on the case. The coroner, Zygmunt Szramka, found the 34-year-old mother of five died after being taken by a shark near Bass Strait's Barrenjoey Island. Mr Szramka's finding, in which he dealt coldly and clinically with provable facts rather than pub gossip, laid no blame. Instead he found 'that in context of recorded shark attacks in Australia and overseas, it was appropriate to make the cautionary observation that the deceased lost her life at a location acknowledged for its increased risk to divers from shark attack, namely a seal colony'.

Diver Fights Shark and Survives

Days after Therese Cartwright's death, a professional diver from Launceston told how he had been attacked by a shark in the same waters only a couple of months previously. Tony Szolomiak, 32, said he thought his time had come but he managed to fight off his attacker. Mr Szolomiak told how he was diving near the seal colony area on Barrenjoey Island when he spotted a three-metre tiger shark heading his way. He was already on the bottom, catching crayfish, when the tiger showed interest in him.

'I saw the shark coming and I said to myself, I'm history, my number's up, I'm going to go,' he told reporters. 'I saw it go past me and then it turned around and I was down kneeling on a rock so it made a beeline for my head. Its mouth was slightly ajar and came within 12 inches [30cm] of my head.'

Mr Szolomiak had been diving for two decades, and said he had spent a lot of time considering the dangers of sharks, reading a lot of books and discussing possibilities with other divers. He stayed on the bottom amongst the rocks, believing that to be the safest course of action. He said he knew he only had one chance, and that was to hit the tiger on the nose as hard as he could because that was its most sensitive spot. As the shark swam past he ducked his head, and gave it a smack with his spear gun, right on the snout. That sent the shark mad, and according to Mr Szolomiak it appeared to go into some sort of convulsion, head down and tail straight up, thrashing around for all it was worth. He seized the opportunity while the shark was distracted, perhaps by pain, to bolt for the surface and clamber back into his boat.

Five years after the death of Therese Cartwright a white pointer began terrorizing professional fishermen in the same area. The rogue shark menaced anglers and divers as well, and tore holes in fishing nets to get at the catch. Spotted and identified as a female six-metre white pointer, the shark roamed along the coast in 1998, patrolling between Lulworth and Weymouth in Noland Bay, around West Sandy Cape and East Sandy Cape to Bridport in Anderson Bay to the east. Fishermen told of holes the size of motor vehicles being torn in their nets as the shark ripped through the material to get at the free meal just on the other side of the tough mesh netting. Enough locals still lived in the area with strong memories of the horror year in 1993 to give some credence to their belief it was the same shark which had taken Therese Cartwright which was now attacking their nets. It was generally regarded as a long term resident of local waters.

Warnings went out to fishermen, divers and surfers to keep a close watch out for the beast. In the pubs where fisherfolk and anyone else who regularly deals with the ocean gather to drink and swap yarns, the warnings were coloured with tales of how a shark that size can rip the outboard motor and transom right out of a good sized fishing boat, sinking it and leaving the occupants floundering helplessly in the water. At the same time, a sudden increase was noticed in the number of savage attacks on seals from the colonies which dot the coastline and offshore reefs and islands.

The fur seals were having a bad year in 1998. Many more than usual horribly injured seals, or the mutilated remains of seals, were found. Conventional wisdom in the area was that white pointers can live to 100 years, and are largely territorial, migrating, if at all, only to breed and then returning to their hunting area. One fisherman told of seeing a white pointer slide noiselessly under his four-metre boat, stretching beyond either end of the hull. The Parks and Wildlife Service, while stopping short of definitely stating the shark cruising nearby waters was the same one which took Therese Cartwright, did acknowledge something unusual was happening. They put it down to a particularly good year for fish breeding in the area, which lifted food stocks and encouraged a good breeding season for the fur seals. This in turn attracted more sharks.

Around the north-east corner of Tasmania that year and about halfway down the east coast, another large shark was making people nervous. The wildlife officials used exemplary understatement to encourage awareness. 'We would advise water-goers in the Triabunna area to bear in mind the fact that there does appear to be a very large shark in the area,' said the official news release. 'It could be inclined to take a bite.'

Perhaps more based on science, a CSIRO shark researcher, Barry Bruce, said at the time the shark which killed Therese Cartwright, and the one which attacked Tony Szolomiak, would be back. Mr Bruce said some sharks returned to the same areas a number of times over several years, and with the Barrenjoey seal colony at Tenth Island still a breeding ground for fur seals, the same sharks would more than likely keep coming back to the same waters. He said there was no reason why a shark should not revisit any area it knows contains food, and sometimes a human could be mistaken for a large fish or, more likely, a seal.

Michael Docherty: Towed by a White Pointer

Not all shark attacks are over in seconds. A swirling disturbance in the water, perhaps a suddenly cut-off scream accompanied by a spreading pool of blood and gore, are the way we mostly think of fatal shark attacks. But this attack was different. Just off the coast near Brisbane, well within sight from the Queensland capital's taller buildings, the Moreton Island surf beaches are a Mecca for surfers from up and down the coast. Michael Docherty, 28, of Palm Beach on the Gold Coast, an easy hour's drive from Brisbane, answered the call to hunt for the perfect wave on a camping and surfing holiday with a pair of surf-seeking friends. They arrived at Moreton Island's North Point Beach on Thursday, 1 October 1992 and set up camp.

It was a spot the group had surfed together and individually for the past decade. By that afternoon Michael was dead, and Australia was stunned once again at the ferocity of the dreaded white pointer. Before Michael and his group arrived, however, there had been talk of a great white in the district. Bill Docherty, Michael's father, said afterwards almost his last words to his son were a warning to be careful and watch out for sharks.

After reaching the island and setting up camp the group

took to the water, Michael wearing a black wetsuit. The three friends began paddling to an area renowned for its right-hand point break, but they were never to get there. Michael was a mere 30 metres from shore, near the edge of a shelf where the ocean floor dropped away and the water suddenly deepened. He was only a few strokes away from waist-deep water, which a four-metre-plus white pointer would almost certainly not have ventured into, when he was knocked from his board about 2.30pm – and a 20-minute saga of horror began.

Up to this point nobody had any idea a large and aggressive shark was even in the area, let alone a 4.2-metre white pointer. The creature clamped its teeth into Michael's body and dragged him under the water, but the leg rope attached to the surfboard refused to break. For 20 minutes the shark dragged Michael's body up and down the beach, towing his surfboard behind all the time. Sometimes the monster broke the surface, still with Michael's body in its jaws according to horrified spectators on the beach. His two camping colleagues, one a Brisbane-based police officer, ran to the tiny North Point settlement to raise the alarm. More than a dozen other surfers watched helpless in terrified fascination from the beach as their brother rider died.

Another policeman, Sgt Phil Sharpe, and a school-teacher on holidays commandeered a small fishing boat and raced towards the North Point Beach as fast as the screaming outboard motor would take them. They shouted and revved the engine on the boat, making as much noise as possible in a bid to frighten the shark off, but all the while it cruised below the surface, its victim still clamped in its murderously efficient jaws and still towing the surfboard. At one stage the boat caught up with the surfboard, standing upright in the water as it was towed along. The policeman and the schoolteacher tried to drag it into the boat but as they hauled it out of the water they saw the shark just below them, and the body of Michael Docherty still in its jaws.

Sgt Sharpe was to tell later how he got a good view of the shark in the clear water off North Point, and that view left him in no doubt it was a white pointer. He recalled it was bigger than the suddenly very flimsy-feeling boat he and the schoolteacher had chosen to do battle with the ocean monster. With more shouting and revving of the motor they were finally able to drive the shark away and retrieve Michael's mauled body, still attached to his board. Sgt Sharpe said it was his impression the shark was playing with its victim, mostly underwater, and the likely cause of Michael's death was drowning.

When Michael's board was finally retrieved it had a dent in it, not a bite, from the shark's initial rush which knocked him into the water. Another Palm Beach surfer who had gone to Moreton Island that day supported the police sergeant's interpretation. Brett Provost, then 25, also had a camera with him, and was able to take pictures from the safety of the beach as the great white towed Michael and his board through the water. He described it as being like a fisherman, playing his catch. 'Everyone felt really helpless. It could have been any one of us out there,' he told reporters.

Eighteen-year-old John Snip from the Gold Coast was also among the horrified crowd watching on the beach. He said the shark towed the board forward and backwards as it changed direction under the water, and told how at least 45 centimetres of its dorsal fin showed above the water during the drama.

At the grieving family's Palm Beach home that night, Michael's father, Bill, said his son was very aware of the dangers he faced in the water. He said Michael fell in love with the outdoor life, especially fishing and surfing, when he was just four years old and knew only too well that the Queensland coast was home to large numbers of sharks. Bill Docherty said Michael told him he'd seen a bronze whaler in the water just the week before on another surfing expedition. Sharks of many types and sizes are not uncommon off Moreton Island, but not the large white pointer, a solitary hunter and usually a deepwater fish. Surfers often told of large schools hanging around, perhaps attracted by the unwanted fish and other waste matter dumped from the trawlers which moored along the coast. They also said the local sharks hadn't been seen in an aggressive mood for many years.

John Wishart: The Attack Watched by Thousands

*I*n 1956 the Olympic Games were coming to Melbourne, World War II was over a decade in the past, and everything in Australia was travelling along quite smoothly. Jobs were plentiful, Holden cars were affordable, and the nation was embarking on an era of getting into the great outdoors. Naturally this included the beaches. Even way back then, Portsea was the favoured hideaway of the well-to-do, but because of their proximity to Melbourne, the Portsea and Sorrento areas also attracted thousands of ordinary Australians to the bay beaches and the back beaches, where the surf rolled in.

Surfers, with their mutual interests, form surfclubs, and naturally clubs compete against each other. Surf carnivals close to Melbourne attracted thousands of spectators, so the tragedy that befell John Wishart affected not only his family and friends, but also the crowds of people lining the high vantage points and the beach. Being close to a major state capital also meant the newspaper reporters of the day were on hand quickly to record the impressions of witnesses for the next day's reading. But even 32 years after the event the impressions of people at Portsea that March day in 1956 were still strong and clear.

Melbourne *Sun* reporter, Bill Hitchings, revisited the Portsea dunes in 1989, and tracked down many of the key players in the tragedy of John Wishart. His report appeared in that newspaper under the headline 'Death from the Deep' (see below):

Death from the Deep

It was a bright, early autumn afternoon. The sun had already headed west over the clifftops behind them but there was still a carnival atmosphere among the 3,000 spectators who packed into the carpark and looked out over the Portsea back beach. It was March 1956 and with the finals of the Sorrento-Portsea Lifesaving Club championships just ended, it was time for some fun.

A handful of the club members had gone out to catch some waves. They were about 300 metres out and their families and friends waved and cheered as they floated ... waiting. There were five of them in a straight line, heads bobbing above the swell. They couldn't hear the crowd over the noise of the surf nor could they see it as they were facing out to sea. John Wishart was on the beach and, like the crowd, could see his mates waiting for the big one.

'I'm going out to catch a wave,' he said to another mate, Roy Boyce, who had just come in after untangling the marker buoys and testing a new waxed nylon rope. John, 26, ran into the surf. His wife of three years, Gloria, 24, and her mother were among the clifftop crowd. John, a Sorrento plumber, was an excellent swimmer and surf skier. He had represented the state in life-saving competitions as well as being a champion footballer in the Mornington Peninsula league. He took up a position to the right of the group. Like them, he watched and waited. Suddenly, he wasn't there anymore. His arms stopped treading their steadying motion through the waves and his blond head disappeared. There was no noise, no cry for help nor a call to his mates. Nothing. Then, just as suddenly, he reappeared. This time his body was caught in the vice-like grip of a shark's jaws. In the numbed eternity of seconds that the brain needs to grasp what the eyes are trying to tell it, each watched silently as the shark held John Wishart aloft. They saw him punch helplessly at the monster that thrashed his body into the surrounding foam …

Among them was John Hopper who saw the shark pass within a metre of him on its frenzied path to its target. 'Get the hell out of here! Get out for God's sake!' John cried. Somehow, all five of them – John Hopper, Tony Woodhouse, 19, of Balwyn, Greg Warland, 20, of the Portsea Officers' Training School, David Crankshaw, 16, of Toorak and Richard Wright, 20, of Camberwell – made it back to the shore. By that time John Wishart had disappeared completely. It was all over in seconds. His body was never found and, despite an intensive search by professional fishermen lasting several weeks, no sign of his remains were found in the dozens of sharks caught in the area. Minutes after the disaster, however, those who saw it spoke of the horror.

'I knew John was dead,' John Hopper said. 'There was a terrible moment as the shark grabbed John. He didn't scream and vanished without a sound. The shark was only three feet [90cm] from me and three quarters out of the water.'

Sam Stirling [John's best mate and captain of the club surfboard crew] saw it all from the clubhouse rooftop. 'I thought it was a porpoise,' he said. 'It was big and black and had a body as wide as a barrel. It was going at such a pace that half the body, from head to tail, was out of the water. It shot between Dave Crankshaw and John Hopper and hit John like a tank. There was a tangle of arms and legs and John disappeared. He came to the surface again and was thrown about by the shark for a second or two and then went under.'

Mr George Bell, of Aspendale, who was with his wife, also saw what happened from the clifftop. 'The swimmer vanished and a few seconds later he was lifted out of the water,' he said. 'I could see to his waist or below and he appeared to be punching at the shark.'

Being still on the beach and so at eye-level to the group, Roy Boyce could not see everything that happened in those few frantic seconds. But this week and now 55, he recalled the shock that filled him, other swimmers and the crowd that afternoon.

'I'll never forget it,' he said. 'It all happened so quickly. One minute John was in the water and the next he was gone.' Mr Boyce, the last person to speak to John Wishart before he disappeared, said he had been out in the surf only minutes before, checking on marker buoys and lines that had become tangled. There was no sign of any trouble although, as he says, there are always sharks off Portsea, heading out of or into Port Phillip Bay. But, he said, the disturbance caused by the tangled lines and their anchors might have attracted one of them.

'Sharks are always unpredictable,' Mr Boyce, now an accountant, said. 'There's no telling what they are going to do or why they do something. But my personal theory – and one that has no official backing – is that one of those sharks must have seen the turbulence and came over to investigate, thinking it was a shoal of fish. Then, on seeing the swimmers, he attacked. But, why the thing went past the others and straight to John is, of course, anyone's guess.'

Hitchings also re-discovered the oddly fatalistic attitude Australians hold towards shark attacks. He concluded, probably quite rightly but never provably so, that the occasional shark fatality, and more common story of survival, will never deter people, even those closely affected, from going back into the water. This applied just as much to John Wishart's family as it did to other witnesses Hitchings spoke to for his article.

His young wife, Gloria, who was with her mother and watched as her husband was killed, discovered soon afterwards that she was pregnant with their first child. Tim, the son John Wishart never knew, went on to become a champion lifesaver and captain of the Portsea Club. Tony Woodhouse, who was one of the five young men who were in the sea only metres from John Wishart when the shark struck, is now Dr Anthony Woodhouse, dental surgeon. He and his wife encouraged their children to take up swimming, particularly in the sea. Two of them joined Point

Leo Surf Lifesaving Club and went on to become champion swimmers. Suzie Woodhouse, now living in Wollongong, captained the Australian women's team several times. And her brother, Olympic bronze medallist Rob, added to his brilliant career by winning the Lorne Pier-to-Pub classic on more than one occasion. Roy Boyce, who was also with John Wishart, went with others back into the sea some weeks later to show there was no real danger. Like Dr Woodhouse, Mr Boyce is still an avid body-surfer and is a life member of the Portsea Club. And the memory of John Wishart is perpetuated by the state's life-saving fraternity. The John Wishart Medal is to surf life-saving what the Brownlow Medal is to Australian Rules football.

(Reproduced by permission of Bill Hitchings and The Herald and Weekly Times.)

Doug Chesser: The Lunch that Cost his Life

A spur of the moment decision to grab a few abalone for an instant meal was the difference between life and death for Douglas Chesser. But it was a perfectly natural act for the 26-year-old fisherman from Port Lincoln in South Australia on that day in June 1998. He loved the sea and had spent all his life around boats. His family was heavily involved in the trade opportunities provided by the ocean. So what could be more second nature than to make a quick lunch straight from the sea? When he was a boy, Doug spent hours crabbing on the beaches around Port Lincoln. In summer he spent so much time surfing his hair looked as if it had been bleached. As he grew older, Doug began 'hooking', or line-fishing, from boats before graduating to the netting of school and gummy sharks that live in the deeper waters off the coast.

About eight months prior to the attack that was to cost him his life, Doug began working on the Chesser family shark-netting boat, *Aquataur*. His deckhand and mate was Neil Jenkins. The two friends had been net fishing for sharks around the islands, about 60 kilometres south of Port Lincoln. About 2pm on Sunday, 28 June, they stopped for lunch, anchoring the *Aquataur* about 200 metres off the north coast of South Neptune Island. They went ashore in a small dinghy and walked about a kilometre to the west coast, where Doug donned his wetsuit and dived into the cold water to collect some abalone off the rocks. He dived into the water and only swam about three metres from the rocky shoreline of the island. Minutes later, a four-metre white pointer shark struck, leaving Doug mortally wounded.

Neil watched in horror, then dived in and grabbed Doug, who was bleeding profusely. He hauled him up on to the flat rocks, already unconscious and losing blood rapidly, then ran about 300 metres up the hill to the only house on the island. There, Sue Cavanagh told him her husband, Roger, was rock fishing about 500 metres south of the flat rocks where Doug had been attacked. Neil ran to fetch him and the two dashed to where Doug lay. But the young diver was dead from loss of blood by the time they reached him.

His father was a fisherman and it was inevitable Doug would be drawn to the blue waters around Port Lincoln. When he died the family was running shark boats, and had recently opened a fish processing factory and outlet, The Fresh Fish Place, in their hometown. The business was run by Doug Chesser snr, and his two sons, Doug and Tommy. The two Dougs were very close, more mates than father and son. They had lived together for several years since the collapse of the marriage of Doug snr and his wife Jo. Sadly, Jo had returned to Port Lincoln with her new husband, Lyndon, on the very weekend her son died. Afterwards the Chesser family gathered at the fish processing factory to try to come to terms with their loss.

Doug's uncle, John, described his nephew as 'one of the most beautifully natured people you can think of. He lived for his fishing and surfing.' John cannot fathom why Doug, an experienced shark fisherman, decided to dive in shark-infested waters for his abalone lunch. 'I'm just in shock,' he said. 'You don't expect a shark is going to be underneath you. He went down for a few abalones. If they wanted to get something to eat why didn't they just eat a can of baked beans?'

Doug Chesser's deckhand and longtime surfing mate, Neil Jenkins, played down his selfless jump into the sea in a vain bid to save his mate. Unwilling to talk about events of that fateful Sunday in detail, he did however deny there were any heroics involved. 'Doug would have done the same for me,' he said afterwards in a simple statement. Jenkins, 22, described his friend with typical Australian understatement as 'a top bloke'.

Neil Jenkins and Doug Chesser had been surfing buddies for years, but recently they had been thrown together a lot more. Over the five months prior to the attack they spent weeks at a time at sea together on board the *Aquataur*. 'We just used to have some good laughs,' Neil said.

While he was playing down his own role in jumping to his mate's rescue, not knowing what lurked in the blood-stained water, another of their friends, Paul Trevor, praised his efforts. 'He's a bloody legend that boy.' Doug Chesser's family had already paid tribute to Neil Jenkins's courage. They said there was no doubt he put his life at risk when he dived into the water and pulled his injured friend to shore. But another friend inside the close-knit fishing community gave a clue that perhaps Doug Chesser enjoyed taking a bit of a risk. David Bailey said his mate was a hard-working fisherman, and 'the gutsiest surfer out there. He was too good a bloke to die.'

Gutsy surfers, who go way out beyond the limits of prudence after the ride of a lifetime, are known in the surfing world as 'sharkbait'. Even at his funeral, the reluctant hero, Neil Jenkins, gave an indication that Doug Chesser may not have considered the dangers before plunging into the water for some lunchtime abalone. He told mourners that he had always looked up to Doug, who never did things by halves, 'always did them to the extreme'.

Afterwards, as the family came to terms with its grief, Doug snr said he was very concerned at some aspects of his son's death. Mr Chesser said there had been 'lots of questions' in his mind about the circumstances of the attack. He was sharply critical of the response time of emergency services in reaching South Neptune Island. He described as 'pathetic' the fact that it took more than five hours for help to reach Neil Jenkins as he sat on the rock shelf next to his mate's dead body. Mr Chesser made the point that if his son had not been as seriously injured as he was in the attack, if there had been a chance to save his life, that chance would have been immeasurably reduced by the delay. He also raised the question of berley[1] (groundbait) being used regularly in the waters around

---

1. Berleying is the practice of spreading fish and animal remains, including blood, in the water and leaving a trail in the ocean currents behind a boat to attract fish. The target fish discover the trail and follow it towards the boat, where they are presented with the baited hooks.

the island to attract sharks, and warned other professional and recreational divers about the danger.

After the attack, there was a lot of ill will among people who use the waters of the Great Australian Bight for various purposes. Other members of the abalone diving community, professional fishers, recreational divers and conservationists, pointed the finger at some commercial tourist operators. They claimed the very white pointer which took Doug Chesser may have been attracted to the area by tourist operators berleying the water with a mixture of fish meat and tuna oil to make sure there were sharks around for their cage-diving expeditions.

The South Australian Shark Fishermen's Association president at the time, Mr Barry Power, said berleying and cage-diving provoked sharks. Another local, who happened to be the Conservation Council marine spokesman, Mr Peter Marchant, who had lived on South Neptune for six years, said he believed berleying attracted the sharks to the island. The Neptune Island group was one of two areas in South Australia at the time where cage dive operators could apply to carry out berleying near land to attract white pointer sharks. For everyone else, the Fisheries Act prohibited berleying with blood, meat and offal within four kilometres of the coast and any islands gazetted as part of South Australia.

What could have turned into a nasty and potentially dangerous dispute was quickly laid to rest by science. Fisheries biologist and shark expert with the CSIRO's Marine Research Unit, Mr Barry Bruce, disputed the claims. 'It [berleying] does not attract sharks from outside the immediate area, but brings the sharks that are in the area together,' he said. The last word on the issue eventually came from the then Mayor of Port Lincoln, Peter Davis. He said Mr Chesser's death was a tragedy for the community and a vivid warning not to dive in shark-infested waters. 'It's rather like running a red light. If you free-dive in one of the world's best places to see great white sharks, it's an inherently dangerous occupation,' he said.

There are many theories about sharks and divers, but one of the more credible ones is that a diver can easily be mistaken by a shark for a seal or sea lion – easy prey for the big hunters of the ocean. The theories are backed up by incidents where sharks have taken a bite at a diver and backed off. It is thought that while the victims may suffer terrible wounds the shark was simply applying the taste test (see page 19 and 226), and decided that neoprene wetsuits, webbing straps and metal tanks are not to its taste. The sharks where Doug Chesser died, it seems, are no exception. They have been seen plucking sea lions off the rocks, actually leaving the water in their hunt for food. Port Lincoln charter boat operator, Bruce Bennett, claims to have seen white pointers sliding onto the flat rocks around the Neptune islands to attack the sea lions.

'These things live and feed near the rocks,' he said. 'I don't think young Doug gave it a thought. The shark probably thought he was a seal. It's not his [the shark's] fault; he's doing what comes naturally.' Mr Bennett said at the time some divers had a gung-ho attitude towards sharks and had asked to be taken shark diving without a cage. He said there were many sharks in the area, as evidenced by another charter operator who attracted seven three-metre sharks during a cage dive on North Neptune Island.

Tragically the white pointer which took Doug Chesser was also linked to a second fatality which added to the woes of the district. The whole Port Lincoln community was devastated by the fisherman's death, but few people were more affected than Scott Nash, a close friend of Mr Chesser. Mr Chesser died on 28 June 1988, and a coronial inquest in December that year found Mr Nash, 25, committed suicide on 15 July by jumping overboard from a trawler 150 kilometres south-west of Ceduna and drowning.

During the inquest one of Mr Nash's friends, Mr Matthew Pinson, said Mr Nash had been 'very emotional after Dougie's death' and 'he could not see a future'. But his mother, Mrs Jennifer Nash, said although her son was upset about Mr Chesser's death he had recovered and was 'in high spirits'. The inquest heard Mr Nash drank heavily after Mr Chesser's funeral on 4 July, which was attended by more than 200 people. After the funeral, he had been employed as a deckhand on the trawler *Comet*, which left Port Lincoln on 7 July for ten days of fishing off Ceduna. During the trip, Mr Nash told his skipper, Mr Tor-Odd Solvester Anderson, it would be his last trip. *Comet's* first mate, Mr Wayne Zemke, told the inquest Mr Nash was 'very mixed up' and 'appeared depressed all the time' while on the trawler.

On the morning of 15 July, Mr Nash told his skipper he had been 'stoned' the previous day. Later that day, Mr Nash exhibited unusual behaviour, including not wearing a top during cold weather and dunking his head in a tank of brine to 'cool off'. Shortly after 3pm, Mr Nash went to the vessel's galley to fetch a bucket, but had not returned after 20 minutes. A concerned Mr Zemke climbed up a ladder and noticed a pair of track pants on the rear right side of the trawler's deck. After searching the boat for Mr Nash, Mr Zemke alerted his skipper and the order was made to raise the nets and return to the position where Mr Nash was thought to have gone overboard. *Comet* zig-zagged the area until dusk, with the crew keeping watch on either side of the trawler and from the wheelhouse.

A comprehensive air and sea search of 1,200 square kilometres of the Great Australian Bight was conducted, but suspended the next day after navy doctors said Mr Nash could only have survived ten hours in the ocean. The coroner, Mr Wayne Chivell, said that on the evidence 'it is appropriate to conclude that Scott Nash had deliberately jumped overboard, with the intention of taking his own life'. Mr Chivell added although Mr Nash's body had never been found, his death was likely caused by drowning.

Doug Chesser and the way he met his death sparked fresh debate around Australia, and especially in South Australia, about the whole issue of killing white pointers. It even led to an editorial in the *Adelaide Advertiser* newspaper (1 July 1998), calling for clear thought and reason to prevail, rather than blind revenge. The newspaper expressed much the same thoughts as were expressed by immediate members of Doug Chesser's family. The editorial was headed 'A Tragedy but no Case for Revenge' (see over).

A Tragedy but no Case for Revenge

The death of fisherman Douglas Chesser, taken by a white pointer shark off the Port Lincoln fishing grounds at the weekend, was a tragedy. Our sympathies go to his family and friends. It was a death which touches on our deepest, instinctive fears, torn and swallowed into the belly of a ferocious fish. But for all the horrors this invokes we use this space today to defend one of the most efficient predators the planet has evolved. We, mankind, have dominion over the seas as well as the earth. We thus also have responsibility. Just as we now provide, on the one hand, a haven for the whales in the sea and, on the other, venomous snakes on land, to exist, breed and nurture their next generation, we should, most warily, be guardians of the white pointers. For all their fearsomeness, in their own habitat they are vulnerable. We could exterminate them just as we almost exterminated the whales. Whales, snakes, all endangered species, the animals are different: the argument is the same. It is in no way odd or bizarre to argue that a proper memorial for Doug Chesser is respect, in its world, for his killer's species and for continuation of the arguments which have advanced its protection.

(Editorial: Adelaide Advertiser, *1 July 1998. Reproduced by permission of The Herald and Weekly Times.)*

Of Horror, Heroism – and Coincidence – at Byron Bay

Byron Bay on the far north coast of New South Wales, so far north it may as well be in Queensland, figures strongly in the shark annals of Australia. Long one of Australia's premier playgrounds because of its climate, the pristine ocean beaches, and accessibility, the area attracts the rich and famous, retirees, honeymooners and the alternative life-stylers. Nimbin, Australia's drop-out capital, is just up the road a bit, inland from Byron Bay and Cape Byron, the most easterly point of the Australian mainland. It is also the scene of one of the most incredibly selfless acts of courage ever recorded on Australian beaches, and the spot where coincidence, years apart, almost defies belief.

The Martin Ford Attack

In 1982, Martin Ford, a 20-year-old surfer from Brisbane, was catching some waves with five friends at Tallow Beach in the bay, just south of Cape Byron. He was 200 metres from shore when his friends saw him just vanish beneath the water. When he surfaced before their startled but still uncomprehending gaze he was screaming for help. His surfing buddies paddled over as fast as they could, still unsure as to what had happened until they got close enough to see the red discoloured water. Not knowing where the shark was, or whether it was making another attack run at Martin or one of them, his friends managed to drag him back onto his surfboard and start for shore.

Agonizing minutes later they reached the sand and were able to take full stock of Marty's savagely mauled legs. They managed to get a tourniquet on one leg while help was being summoned, and an ambulance was there within minutes. Marty Ford was barely conscious when his friends, still hopeful he would live, saw him safely placed in the back of the ambulance, which raced away from the beach towards Byron Bay Hospital. By the time he arrived at casualty he was unconscious, and soon afterwards, having lost so much blood and going into deep shock, he was dead. Marty Ford was the first person to be killed by a shark in New South Wales for 19 years.

The John Ford Attack

The next fatal attack was to come 11 years later, also at Byron Bay, and the victim was John Ford. John and Debbie Ford had been married for 15 days and were on their honeymoon from Sydney when John gave up his life to save that of his new bride. Both were experienced divers, certified for open ocean waters, so the peaceful haven of Byron Bay presented no dangers in that regard. A local diving instructor estimated 50,000 people visited the spot each year. The Fords, of Harbord, were diving with three other people off Julian Rocks, two kilometres from Cape Byron, when the shark attacked about 9.30am. The attack happened at an area called Mackerel Boulder, a popular diving destination just north of Julian Rocks, known to locals as 'Spot X'.

The group was on an organized diving trip with Sundive Dive Centre, a reputable local company which operated out of Byron Bay. Less than a week earlier, newspapers around Australia had run stories about Therese Cartwright being killed by a white pointer while diving near a seal colony in Tasmania (see page 50). However, nobody in the party that day was concerned. There were no seal colonies in Byron Bay, and white pointers were a rarity in the warmer waters that far north, preferring the cooler southern currents. But sharks were still on their minds, because part of the dive-mission that day was to observe Byron Bay's grey nurse sharks.

The whole group had been in the water for some time, and was about to surface to replenish their air supply when the shark struck. They had gathered a few metres below the surface, holding on to the anchor line of their dive boat, for a decompression safety stop. To their amazement a 5.5-metre white pointer appeared beneath them. The ghostly shape turned and headed towards Debbie, when John suddenly grabbed her and pushed her out of the way, placing himself between his bride and the shark.

What followed is the stuff of horror stories. John Ford literally disappeared into the jaws of the giant under the horrified gaze of his wife and the three other members of the diving party. Even as they rocketed to the surface and scrambled aboard their boat, they knew there was no chance. Debbie, understandably hysterical, had to be helped aboard, and the alarm was raised within seconds. She was to learn later that John had been bitten in half by the monster.

A search was quickly started for the shark in case it was still around, and for the body of John Ford or whatever remained of it. Some locals with intimate knowledge of the seas in the area were called in to help, and to catch the killer if possible. Their story alone is shocking. Gavin Dwyer and Ron Boggis, both professional fishermen, and retired shark catcher Terry Bertoli, rushed to Julian Rocks in their shark boat. Within a couple of hours of the attack they had hooked a white pointer, using a mackerel tuna on a seven-mm rope, attached to a 2000-pound [approximately 1000-kilogram] catwire trace, a virtually unbreakable rig, even for the biggest shark.

Mr Dwyer said the white pointer was fractionally bigger than his 5.8-metre fishing boat. 'It took a lot of rope in the struggle, but if we had had a 303 on board the shark would have been finished pretty quickly,' he said. 'It took four of us to hold him, but he was still taking a lot of line … That thing was as big as a truck. We had it so close to the boat a couple of times we could have had a picnic on its back.

'Words can't really describe what it was like out there. It was an unbelievable fish, an absolute monster. It is something that will live in my memory for the rest of my life.'

At that stage they did not know for certain they had hooked the white pointer that took John Ford, although it was very likely given the rarity of the great whites in Byron Bay. Proof they got the right animal was not long in coming. During the titanic 90-minute battle the shark regurgitated

Mr Ford's torso and part of his wetsuit. It also towed the heavy fishing boat six kilometres out to sea. But on this occasion, the shark was more than a match for the human posse. The fishermen said they had pulled the shark alongside their boat three times. They looked ill themselves when they told how, after an hour of fighting, it had vomited up the torso. Mr Boggis, emotionally and physically drained, said the exhausted white pointer had been badly injured in the struggle but still had enough energy for one last dive. At the bottom of the dive, the catwire trace had snapped under its enormous weight. The men went back the following day in another bid to track the killer shark, but were unsuccessful.

'I'm just disappointed for the poor man's wife,' Mr Boggis said. 'We wanted to get it bloody bad for the sake of that poor woman. It would have been nice to get that big bastard out of the water for good so it couldn't do this sort of thing again. When we saw him spitting out the bloke's body it made us more determined to catch it and kill it.'

Mr Dwyer said after the unsuccessful hunt that the shark was a whole new experience for him. 'It was as round as the back of our boat, the biggest I have ever seen in 25 years on the water,' he said, awestruck. 'It's a female and a loner. You can tell its sex by the size of its fins.' Mr Bertoli said the white pointer had been trying to head north throughout the struggle. 'I wouldn't be going swimming on the Gold Coast,' he said.

Soon after the attack and still on the beach, Debbie Ford used a mobile phone to call her parents, Kevin and

Jan Holm, who left their Sydney home immediately to join their just-widowed daughter. Mr Holm described John Ford as a 'tremendous fellow' who had saved his daughter with a 'selfless act of courage that would never be forgotten. They were side by side when it happened. They were decompressing and were about three metres below the surface when the shark came from below them. John pulled her out of the way and that was it.'

'He was a wonderful husband and he always looked after me,' Debbie said as the search for her husband's body and the killer shark continued. 'He was protecting me. He pushed me away from the shark. He was a hero and a great husband and I loved him dearly. He gave his life for me.'

The day after John Ford's ultimate act of heroism, Debbie and her parents were taken by a Sundive Dive Centre speedboat back to Julian Rocks for a private memorial ceremony. Mrs Ford said she spoke about the attack because she wanted the world to know how brave her husband had been. The hunt for the great white and John Ford's remains continued after the memorial service. Parts of his wetsuit, his flippers, airtank and weight belt were found, but there was no further sign of the man-eating shark.

'We are going to continue the search just in case other body parts are found,' said Inspector Chris Long of Byron Bay police. 'I think any reasonable person would not want to go swimming out there at the moment.'

His colleague, Snr-Sgt Kevin Jones, appealed for calm, putting the attack down to 'freakish bad luck'. But calm was not what the water-loving population of northern New

South Wales and southern Queensland wanted. Everybody who had suitable gear was after the killer of John Ford. Heavy duty static shark lines were set up and down the Sunshine and Gold coasts. A fisherman off Bribie Island caught a white pointer on one of his lines only a few hundred metres off a popular beach. It was 4.5 metres long, tipped the scales at one tonne, and came close several times to swamping the fishing boat as it thrashed around in the water after being tied to the stern. When it was cut open, its stomach was empty. That shark was an innocent victim.

Back at Byron Bay a low-key search and a high-level watch was maintained. A few days after the tragedy, other body parts of John Ford were found, and about a week afterwards his head was discovered on the floor of the bay. The local high school also cancelled a planned surfing trip to Tallow Beach, the same beach at which Marty Ford was taken in 1982. Enough of John Ford's body was recovered to enable the family to hold a funeral service back in Sydney, rather than just a memorial ceremony. An emotional 300 mourners packed a northern Sydney church for the service and funeral of the 31-year-old newlywed. Debbie had to be supported by her parents, Kevin and Jan, throughout the proceedings. John Ford's brother, Michael, bought the entire crowd to the verge of tears as he choked back his own emotions and told the crowd how John and Debbie had known each other for about 18 months, but had never been happier than the day they were married, a mere 15 days before John died.

'I remember when John rang me at work to say he and Debbie were engaged,' he told the mourners. 'I lightheartedly told him he must be kidding and I asked him why. He replied simply "Because I love her".'

Even in the face of tragedy, perhaps especially in the face of tragedy, Australians seem to find ways of including humour in their coping mechanism. It's not always in the best of taste, but it is always there and always will be. Which is probably why, in the pubs of Byron Bay to this day somebody is likely to burst into song whenever talk turns to sharks. The song is invariably a simple ditty based on the advertising slogan used by one of our big car manufacturers: 'Have you eaten a Ford lately'.

Tragic End for a University Diving Club Member

There was never any doubt when it came to the coronial inquest on Jonathan Lee. His death was witnessed by an off-duty policeman, a trained observer whose day-to-day job involved being aware of what was happening around him and being able to recall events accurately and completely. But that did not reduce the level of tragedy.

Jonathan was one of five children who had lived with his family on their hobby farm at One Tree Hill for more than five years before moving to live in residence at St Mark's College when he enrolled at Adelaide University. A bright teenage student, part of a large and happy family and a recreational diver, he was following all the safety rules bar one. The policeman witness could answer all the questions about what happened, but nobody could positively answer the one about why it happened.

Jonathan Lee was 19 and in his second year at Adelaide University when he went diving with the university skin-diving club in September, 1991. He had joined the skin-diving club at the start of that year, and seven other club members were with him on the Sunday diving trip to Aldinga, south of Adelaide. They boarded the dive boat and powered off to Snapper Point, dropping anchor only 350 metres offshore. They picked a spot known as the drop-off, where there was a shelf and the water depth increased to about 18 metres. Snapper Point is named because of the good snapper-fishing in the area. But sharks also eat snapper.

One of Jonathan's fellow divers that day was Sen-Constable Dave Roberts, off-duty and looking forward to a relaxing Sunday outing. He said afterwards he was certain the shark was a white pointer, and it would have been about four metres long. Sen-Constable Roberts was within two metres of Jonathan when the shark struck, but despite being so close he had no warning of the impending attack. He said the first inkling he had of any danger was hearing a thunderous roar.

'It literally sounded like a huge boat coming straight over the top of me' he said. 'I looked to my left-hand side. I saw the shark and I could actually see Jonathan at that stage. I wasn't exactly sure what was happening, but it was thrashing its head out from side to side very violently. Then I made out the shape of the wetsuit. I wasn't able to distinguish clearly any of the features but it was quite apparent that he didn't have anything else in its mouth apart from my buddy. I could think about nothing else except trying to save him and then trying to save both of us. The absolute violence of the attack was just awesome. I have never seen anything like it. The thrashing seemed to stop and the shark disappeared and I was just left in a cloud of bloodied water with no visibility at all. Figured that it couldn't see me if I couldn't see it.'

But it soon became clear to Sen-Constable Roberts nothing could be done. 'It's a horrific way to lose somebody,' he said. 'It would have been an extremely quick and painless sensation.'

It seems none of the other university divers saw or heard a thing. The policeman kicked to the surface and raised the alarm, shouting to four other members of the dive group who had already got back into their boat. Two others still in the water started an immediate search but found no sign whatsoever of their dive-buddy. A much more thorough search was hastily organized the same day, but only managed to turn up confirmation that Jonathan had been taken by a shark, and there was no chance for his survival. The searchers found only a small portion of his body, his flippers and his air tank with its hose severed.

The following day, Monday, a major search was launched. Police divers armed themselves with powerheads, spear-gun-like devices that fire a shotgun or rifle charge, in case the killer shark was still about, and went into the water. A rescue helicopter quartered the ocean from above, with another policeman aboard keeping watch on the divers, and more police were on a boat watching for the shark. One of the officers on the boat was armed with a high-powered rifle. Along the shoreline and in the water surrounding the focal point of the police search, Coast Guard and Sea Rescue volunteers also scoured the area. They were searching, in vain as it turned out, for anything which may have floated along the coast or been washed ashore. Weather and sea conditions conspired against the searchers.

When the police divers went into the 18-metre deep water at the drop-off, visibility was at about six metres, but a few hours later, by early afternoon, it had halved. The search was called off for the day with absolutely no further trace of Jonathan Lee being found. Nor was there a single shark sighted by the divers, the boat crew or the watchful eye-in-the-sky. After the attack the South Australian Fisheries department warned Aldinga fishermen not to try to lure the shark back to the area to catch it. They were told all that would do would be to attract other sharks to their beaches.

Fisheries director, Rob Lewis, said people should not burley the area because the chance of catching the shark responsible for the attack was extraordinarily low. 'I don't want to be ghoulish about this but the chance of the shark needing to feed again for some days is extremely low,' he said. 'It is possible the shark has gone a long distance by now.'

Mr Lewis said white pointers were known to inhabit all areas of St Vincent Gulf, and they also had their favoured areas to hunt and feed. About a week before the attack on Jonathan Lee, a group of commercial divers had sighted a white pointer in the waters off Aldinga. They said it was a similar size to the one which took Jonathan, but the department said there was no way anyone could ever tell if it was the same animal. The department moved quickly to stop any wholesale slaughter of sharks, because the very day after Jonathan's death there were calls of a massive culling programme to rid South Australia of the menace.

At a news conference in the days after the attack, Sen-

Constable Roberts said there was no cause to take revenge on the white pointers. At the conference, Mr Roberts several times described white pointers as 'graceful' but dangerous, unpredictable creatures. 'I don't think that by going out and destroying something we are going to achieve much,' he said. 'When nature takes its turn, it takes over control and there is nothing you can do about it. I would not like to take revenge on that particular creature.'

It was at that conference that Sen-Constable Roberts revealed the one and only safety breach which may have encouraged the attack. It was a breach that divers, including members of the Adelaide University dive club, had been getting away with for years, without being attacked. It was also a breach which was largely unavoidable because of the diving equipment available at the time.

Dave Roberts said both he and Jonathan had been wearing old, black wetsuits and the shark may have mistaken them for one of its favourite foods, seals.

The School Excursion that Ended in Horror

*I*t was a perfect day for the bunch of kids from Sarina High School when they set off for a school outing to the beach on the central Queensland coast. The school chartered two buses to take 130 students and nine teachers on their annual Christmas break-up excursion. The world was very close to perfect as the children arrived at Black's Beach, about ten kilometres north of Mackay. It was the last day of November, 1984, a Friday, the end of the school week, with summer, school holidays and Christmas just around the corner.

They leapt on the catamarans, surf skis and wind surfers hired from the Black's Beach Aqua Park and took to the water. About 60 children were in the water when four of the boys, Nicholaas Bos, Darren Keating, Mark Scott and Chris Petersen, year 10 classmates, snared a catamaran, giving not a thought to the number on the sail – 13. The young and inexperienced sailors were having the time of their lives 300–400 metres offshore, and it was even funnier when Nicholaas fell overboard. His mates tossed him a life-jacket and began manoeuvring the small catamaran to pick him up, still laughing and starting to think about lunch. It was just on 12.30pm.

Darren said later he heard 'half a yell' from Nicholaas just as they turned the boat around, then the water around their friend turned red, and a sinister black fin broke the surface. 'As soon as I looked over the boat and saw all the blood, I knew it was a shark,' he said two days later.

The boys pulled their mortally wounded friend back onto the catamaran, and with panic adding to their lack of sailing experience began making their erratic way back to shore. Nicholaas was unconscious when his mates got him back on board, but he died within minutes and there was nothing that could be done for him on the sand at Black's Beach. A local doctor, summoned by a frantic phone call from the part owner of the aqua park, Jan Parkinson, said the youngster had lost a lot of blood, and probably died from shock within minutes of being attacked. The shark – believed to be a tiger shark – was about four metres long and Darren said it appeared to head out to sea after launching its fatal attack on Nicholaas.

It made only a single pass at its teenage victim. Resort staff quickly took to the water in outboard powered dinghies, herding the rest of the frolicking children to shore, where teachers could do nothing except try to keep them calm and prevent panic breaking out. News of the attack spread within hours, and for the rest of the weekend, up and down the coast around Mackay, beaches were largely deserted as police issued warnings through local radio stations that the shark could attack again.

Even though Darren Keating said a trail of blood in the water seconds after the attack indicated the shark was heading out to sea, there were some efforts to catch the beast. But red tape intervened. Jan Parkinson's husband, Craig, wanted to join contract shark fisherman Ken Humphreys in attempts to catch the killer, but was warned off by a local Fisheries officer because he did not have the proper permits. Mr Humphreys was able to set ten drum lines – moored lines attached to buoys – but to no avail. Two days after the attack at Black's Beach a fisherman caught a 3.2- metre tiger shark in his bait net, more than 50 kilometres north of Mackay, near the crowded tourist resort at Airlie Beach, but it could not be determined if it was the Black's Beach killer.

Beaurepaire, Chalmers: The Coogee Tragedy

*I*t was a still hot day on eastern Sydney's Coogee Beach. On the sand, under a cloudless high-summer sky, families picnicked. A vendor sold ice-creams from a wheeled cart. In the shallows close to shore, couples splashed about, some playing ball with their children. Further out, young lifesavers were catching as many waves as they could find before that weekend's surf carnival began. The date was Saturday 4 February 1922: a day that would forever be remembered as a time of stark horror – and of astonishing courage.

The seeds of the tragedy were sown thus: An 18-year-old lifesaver, Milton Coughlan, swam with two friends to what popularly was known as The Reef, about 40 metres off the clubhouse rocks. The trio performed an unofficial pre-carnival warm-up for the 6,000 spectators lining the shore. Milton earned particular applause for what later would be described as 'a fine shoot' – riding a hurtling wave into a channel between reef and beach, where the water was only waist deep. It was from this vantage point that he noticed two sleek black shadows speeding toward his friends. Cupping hands to his mouth he shouted a warning: 'Sharks! Swim for your lives!'

The young lifesavers needed no further urging – and reached shore safely. Milton in turn began a leisurely swim back to the beach. It was then, as the crowd watched helplessly, that the tragedy struck. A third shark, unseen until now, suddenly hurled itself at Milton Coughlan – hitting him with such terrible force that he was flung into the air. When he fell back he tried desperately to beat the predator off. But it was an uneven fight. While the carnival crowd watched helplessly the shark tore one of his arms off at the elbow. On the beach Milton's fellow-lifesavers exploded into action. A reel-carrying team formed instantly, pushed through dumbstruck spectators and headed for the rocks. The weed-slicked surfaces were slippery, causing several members of the group to lose their footing. Among them was a local swimmer, Jack Chalmers, who had served as a digger in World War I, concluded only four years earlier.

Chalmers slipped particularly badly on the treacherous rocks, striking his head and skinning both shins, which began to stream with blood. But the pain did not deter him. A witness later recalled: 'He was just determined to get out there and nothing would hold him back. Someone tried to fit him with the regulation belt, but he refused, saying "No time!" Instead he tied the reel around his waist and plunged straight into the water.'

Dazed and half-stunned though he was, Jack Chalmers swam out to the stricken lifesaver at what the *Sydney Mail* described as 'extraordinary' speed. 'Around poor Coughlan,' wrote the *Mail*'s reporter, 'there could be seen a circle of blood. With wonderful presence of mind at such a moment, he turned round in order to help his rescuer as much as possible. Coughlan was torn about, and he must have been suffering terribly from both pain and shock; but he did everything in his extremity to help Chalmers, whose work constitutes one of the finest acts of heroism seen on our beaches. He had only a bare line round him and those holding it had to be careful in working it.'

Milton and his would-be rescuer were in appalling trouble. The shark, frenzied by the blood foaming from its victim, circled, trying for a further bite, while Jack Chalmers tried to hold it off with his shoulders and fists. The shark prevailed, clamping its teeth onto the teenager again. Refusing to give up, Chalmers grabbed the dying boy and literally pulled him from the man-eater's jaws. Although the struggle had lasted no more than seconds, Chalmers was growing weak now. He later admitted that he had 'almost' resigned himself to death.

But help was coming. Frank Beaurepaire, short, square-shouldered and one of Australia's greatest sportsmen, had begun running for the ocean the moment he learned of the attack. Swimming past panicking swimmers who were headed in the opposite direction, Beaurepaire went straight to the nightmare scene and, aided by the reel-operators, managed to help Chalmers and Coughlan back to shore. At that time, the 31-year-old Beaurepaire held more than 200 swimming titles from Britain, Europe, the United States, Canada, South Africa, New Zealand and his native Australia. But the newspapers – and the public – agreed that during those few perilous minutes at Coogee Beach he had performed the noblest feat of his career. Sadly, however, the rescue effort had been in vain. So hideously injured was Milton Coughlan, and so massive his loss of blood, that he died soon after an ambulance had delivered him to a Sydney hospital.

Milton's memorial still stands in Randwick Cemetery. The heroism of Chalmers and Beaurepaire made headlines around the world and won them numerous awards. The Royal Humane Society gave the two men its highest honour – the Gold Medal for Bravery. King George V later awarded his Albert Medal for courage – and the Surf Lifesaving Association of New South Wales gave the pair its Merit Award for conspicuous bravery in the surf.

Australia's people said thanks in a more practical way – by giving the rescuers £3,000 ($6,000) raised through a public subscription initiated by Sydney's Lord Mayor. The money was a fortune in those times – enough to buy six or seven suburban houses. Frank Beaurepaire used his share to start an enterprise that would help change the nation's business history. Within ten years his Beaurepaire Tyre Service would be one of Australia's biggest companies, employing more than 4,500 workers – and enabling the newly-minted millionaire and his wife to become philanthropists on an unprecedented scale.

Beaurepaire's influence was powerful on a local level, too. One month after he risked his life to save Milton Coughlan, Coogee's residents were shaken by a second shark attack – and they turned to Beaurepaire, always a natural leader, to advise them what to do. The victim this time was a young man, Martin Gannon, who was mauled while enjoying an afternoon swim. He died of his injuries on 4 March 1922. One newspaper reported that his death was caused by 'gas gangrene on the buttocks.' Beaurepaire told reporters that 'some kind of shark fence' was vital for swimmers' safety. This preliminary idea would inspire an inventor to develop a revolutionary anti-shark solution.

But the local Surf Lifesaving Brigade was naturally more concerned with the immediate problem. Members voted to offer rewards for all sharks caught at Coogee during the rest of March. The brigade published a list of conditions which by modern standards seems somewhat bizarre:

Sharks must be caught in Coogee Bay.

Onus of proof to be on claimant. Sharks must be over three feet [90 centimetres] long and caught in March, 1922. Claimants to report to Mr F. O'Grady, council's caretaker of surf sheds, before cutting up shark. Mr O'Grady to measure length. Any dispute to be referred to Mr Paterson, President of New South Wales Surf Lifesaving Association. If Mr O'Grady is satisfied, jaws to be cut out, given to him, labelled and kept for Mr Paterson. Mr O'Grady to give a receipt to the claimant, who may then lodge claim with it. If the shark is over four feet [1.2 metres] long the stomach is to be removed but not opened until Mr Paterson is present. Bonus £5 [$10] each for the first 12 sharks caught under these conditions. Additional £45 [$90] bonus for the shark which attacked Mr Coughlan and Mr Gannon, if it can be identified to the satisfaction of Mr Paterson [who is] to be the sole judge in every dispute.'

Dynamite – and Record Crowds

So anxious were the local lifesavers to rid their seas of killers that they applied for – and received – a Fisheries department permit to blow sharks out of Coogee Bay with dynamite. The explosives were never used – but immediately the rewards were announced, the suburb found itself besieged by flotillas of big-game chasers gung-ho to haul in a man-eater. Three members of this new breed of bounty hunters deposited the first shark – 'a 'monster' – on Coogee beach on Friday 3 March 1922. But the bathing sheds manager disappointed the men by ruling that as the creature had been caught 'outside the Coogee boundary' it didn't qualify for a reward.

The shark-catchers' argument that their quarry had been headed straight for Coogee cut no mustard with the pennywise but palpably shark-foolish official. However, other bonus-seekers were not deterred. On the following Sunday the suburb was besieged by the biggest crowds in its history. The *Sydney Mail* reported: 'Never before has such an enormous number of people congregated in Coogee … In the afternoon the number of tramcars rapidly increased until there was an almost unbroken line of them from the ambulance station to the terminus. Every tramcar was crowded … and it was quite impossible for many people at Circular Quay and Bondi Junction to get aboard. Enormous numbers of motor cars and motor cycles were parked closely together in every point [offering] a view of the ocean. Every hill in the neighbourhood was black with people.'

The estimated 80,000 crowd had come to Coogee seeking a sensation – and the crew of the steamer *Pacifique,* then in port, tried hard to provide one. According to the *Mail:* 'Nine stalwart natives of the Loyalty Islands, accompanied by two officers of the ship arrived, and attired in quaint bathing costumes plunged into the sea off the rocks. They swam out to the outer buoy [a kerosene tin] and dived down to see if there were any sharks near the bait. Each man was armed with a sheath knife and a keenly-pointed marlinspike about 12 inches [30 centimetres] long. Either weapon would be used with deadly effect if a shark came close. However, they were not able to find any trace of sharks and [instead] swam leisurely towards the shore, entertaining the onlookers with remarkable exhibitions of diving and swimming. The lifesaving club took up a collection for these hardy sailors.'

Despite the revenue the sightseers and bonus-seekers had brought with them, the local council was less than pleased. Far from solving the problem, the offer of bounties simply brought a circus to Coogee. But solutions were slowly emerging. The celebrity conferred on the area by the heroism of Beaurepaire and Chalmers ensured the council was always taken seriously when it sought money to fund its fight against sharks. In 1929 the mayor announced that his council intended – in some way – to sharkproof the suburb's beaches – and called for ideas. More than 300 companies and individuals responded, with engineering plans costing between £5,000 and £70,000 ($10,000 and $140,000). The lowest tenderer got the job.

Designer Frank O'Grady's idea was a huge net 760 feet

[231.5 metres] long, cunningly 'woven' from galvanized steel suspended from pulleys on a steel cable. The Melbourne *Herald* (21 May 1929) reported: 'A rigid fence would not be effective, because channels [would] form underneath, allowing sharks to pass through. [By contrast] a heavy chain running along the bottom will keep the net on the seabed. It [will] be the first sharkproof enclosure erected in Australia.'

The revolutionary sea-fortress – which would be copied around the world – was opened in November 1929. For a toll of one penny, beachgoers could swim without fear. Those who begrudged the money could dive into the waves, without charge, from the northern part of the beach. This stretch of toll-free sand was known locally as 'the Scotsman's End'. Happily, the toll-evading swimmers went unpunished for their thrift. For the 14 years to 1943, when wartime steel shortages made it impossible to maintain the net, there were no further shark attacks at either end of the popular beach.

Frank Beaurepaire, whose unselfish actions and cash gifts had done so much for Coogee, moved to Melbourne, where he became Lord Mayor in October 1940. He became a member of Victoria's Legislative Council – and subsequently gave $400,000 to Melbourne University to found the Frank Beaurepaire Physical Education Centre. Late in his life he played a major part in winning the Olympic Games for Melbourne. But he did not see the results of his efforts. Three months before the 1956 Games began, a massive heart attack ended his brilliant life.

(Reproduced by permission of John Pinkney.)

Shark Claims Champion Bowler

Bob Purcell, former Commonwealth Games bowler, loved to take an early-morning swim in Burleigh Lake, which backed on to his Gold Coast house. But at around 6.30am on 8 February 2003, tragedy struck.

Mr Purcell, 84, was attacked by what police believe was a 2.5-metre bull whaler shark. Kayakers found his body, which had severe leg injuries, three hours after he disappeared.

Officials from Queensland's department of Primary Industries immediately set shark-trapping nets and baited drum lines in the lake and its surrounding canals, in the hope of catching the shark. Next day these traps snared three bull sharks. But analysis of their stomach contents showed that none had attacked Mr Purcell.

Bob Purcell's death was the second in two months. In December, 23-year-old Beau Martin had been killed by a shark in nearby Miami Lake.

The Primary Industries minister, Henry Palaszczuk, repeated his warning that people should avoid swimming in coastal canals, creeks and lakes.

The waterways are plagued by hundreds of bull whalers – also known as river whalers because of their habit of hunting beneath inland waters. These sharks habitually disable their prey, then swim away before returning later to eat.

The Queensland government regularly advises people to swim in pools or between the flags.

Tony Ham, manager of Queensland's shark patrol programme, blamed the drought for the 'teeming numbers' of sharks in the canals. 'The drought means less fresh water is running into the canals, making them saltier. This has led to greater numbers of saltwater fish entering the canals – and the bull sharks follow them, after which they move further upstream.'

(Reproduced by permission of John Pinkney.)

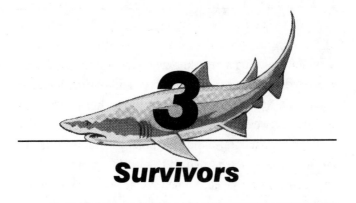

Survivors

Rodney Fox: 'Miracle Man'

One of Australia's best-known shark experts is Rodney Fox. He has looked them in the eye and felt the power of their bite. Neither a scientist nor researcher by training, he does, however, probably know as much about sharks, their habits, habitats and psychology as anyone in the world. He is also regarded as the world's most fortunate man, having survived, somehow, an extremely serious attack by a white pointer which was hell-bent on making him a meal. His chest and torso were literally torn apart by the shark's teeth and he needed well over 400 stitches just to get everything roughly back into shape. He lost litres of blood and kilograms of flesh and muscle, and by rights should have died that day in December, 1963. Fortunately for the future of shark research, and in a way fortunately for all great whites, he didn't die. He instead became a champion for the cause of the great whites, and provides a counterpoint to the arguments of some other shark experts who believe they should not be protected and should be hunted down mercilessly if they so much as look sideways at a swimmer or surfer.

Rodney Fox, like all shark attack survivors, remembers clearly what happened to him. He is able to replay the terrifying few seconds over and over in slow motion in his mind, reliving it as if it were yesterday. And if his imagination and memory aren't enough, he has a permanent reminder, in the form of a piece of shark tooth embedded in his wrist.

Fox was 27 and worked as an insurance salesman in Adelaide when he had his encounter. He was a keen diver, and was competing in the South Australian spear fishing and skindiving championships in December, 1961. The championships were being held in St Vincent's Gulf, off Aldinga Beach, about 90 kilometres south of Adelaide. Fox has told his story many times, and his own words are still the best to relay the terrifying detail of his ordeal. It started when he dived after a large morwong, his target for the competition, and he remembers that under the rules in place at the time it was snorkels and flippers only; no scuba gear was allowed at this contest. Fox was about 12 metres down and concentrating intently on his prized morwong:

How can I describe the sudden silence? It was a perceptible hush, even in that quiet world, a motionlessness that was somehow communicable, deep below the surface of the sea. Then something huge hit me with tremendous force on my left side and heaved me through the water. I was dumbfounded. Now the 'thing' was pushing me through the water with wild speed and I felt a bewildering sense of nausea. The pressure on my back and chest was immense. A queer 'cushioning' feeling ran down my right side as if my insides on my left were being squeezed over to my right side. I had lost my face mask and I could not see in the blur. My spear-gun was knocked violently out of my hand. The pressure on my body seemed to be actually choking me. I didn't understand what was happening. I tried to shake myself loose but found my body was clamped, as if in a vice. With awful revulsion my mind came into focus and I realized: The shark had me in its jaws.

That was just the start of Rodney Fox's battle with the great white. Fox tells how he fought blindly, becoming desperate for air. Remember, he had no scuba tank, and the great white's teeth had broken every rib on one side of his body and perforated a lung. He managed to gouge the beast in one of its soulless eyes, something the shark would not have been expecting, and perhaps that is why it relaxed its jaws a little.

Operating on blind instinct Fox wrenched and ripped himself free, heedless of the further damage he was doing to his body. Floating in a cloud of his own blood, he tells of the terror as the fish came at him again, its great head coming for him through the red-stained water. He tried to push himself away from the shark, aiming a blow at its snout, but its jaws had opened again and his right arm went straight into its mouth. The slashed and torn flesh on his arm alone later required 94 stitches to repair.

Desperate for air, Fox kicked his way to the surface, bumping against the beast's rough skin a number of times on the way up. He managed a few gulps of air only to have the shark come at him again. Its fin brushed against his swim flippers, and thinking only to avoid the horrifying jaws, he wrapped his legs around the great beast's body. It dived, so deep that Rodney Fox scraped the rocks on the ocean floor. Struggling to the surface again Fox gasped more life-giving air, but he recalls the shark had not quite finished with him yet.

'The shark hit surface a few feet away … its hideous body was like a great rolling tree trunk, but rust-coloured, with a great pectoral fin. The ultimate horror was that it was my master. I was alone in its domain. Here the shark made the rules. I was no longer an Adelaide insurance salesman. I was something to eat.'

He recalls shouting 'Shark! Shark!' and then seeing it coming towards him for what must surely be the last time, but it veered aside and vanished into the depths. Fortunately, because of the skindiving competition, there were plenty of boats around, and within seconds Rodney Fox was hauled from the water, horribly mutilated, and on his way to shore, and then to the emergency operating room in hospital. When he arrived it was discovered he had literally almost been bitten in half, and was being held together by the remains of his wet-suit.

As if one was not enough, he described in another interview his second near-death experience of the day as he lay under the bright operating theatre light. 'While they were operating, I was fixated on that light as if it were my link to life, because I was very weak from the wounds and shock,' he said. 'There was one point where the light seemed to get smaller and farther away. I found myself having to fight to keep that light from going out; somehow if it went out I knew I'd be gone. I willed that light to get larger.'

Fox is nothing short of a walking miracle. In hospital it was discovered, once the blood had been cleaned away, that his abdomen was fully exposed and all the ribs on his left side were broken. His diaphragm was punctured, a lung was torn open, his scapula (shoulder blade) was pierced, his spleen was uncovered, a main artery from his heart was exposed, and he was seconds away from his major blood vessels collapsing because of the amount of blood he had lost. He also suffered damage to the tendons, fingers and thumb on his lacerated right arm. Somehow surgeon Justin Miller managed to piece everything together, and eventually used 462 stitches. Fox was in hospital for five months, and the pictures of the wounds he suffered, and their aftermath scarring, flashed around the world, leaving millions shivering at the power of the great white, and wondering how one man could survive such ferocity.

Rodney Fox Fact File

• Many shark attack survivors shun the water for years – or a lifetime. But Rodney Fox swam in the sea only 13 weeks after the great white almost bit him in half. He has recalled in interviews how his wife paddled him on a large board amidst several dozen other divers. 'I was scared and still very weak that first time,' he told a reporter. 'I kept seeing sharks [imaginary ones] coming at me from every direction. But I gave myself a talking to … shook my head and got rid of those phantom attackers. After that I was gradually able to start enjoying the sea again.'

• The commonest question Rodney Fox is asked is *what to do* if a shark approaches. 'If you know the shark's there, you're halfway toward surviving,' he said. 'Most victims don't see the shark coming – its strategy of attack is to come at you from behind. So if you let it know you've seen it, you're doing well. You should keep your eye on the shark all the time.

'Move steadily – no splashing or panic – to the shore or the boat or another group of people. The shark's probably looking to see if you're wounded, so it's essential to *look* calm, even though you mightn't be feeling that way inside.'

• *But what if the shark attacks?* 'It's essential to fight – as hard as you can. Use your surfboard, punch or kick – whatever you can do.'

• *Do sharks actively want to eat people?* 'Probably not. Their normal food is animals like seals and dolphins – and they attack these on the water surface.

When a dolphin or seal surfaces to breathe, its sight and sonar can be confused by the waves – so the shark knows that's the best time to attack. Probably, in many attacks, the shark has confused a human swimmer for a dolphin or seal.'

• Despite his nightmare experience in 1961, Rodney Fox is a major campaigner for the protection of sharks. His Fox Shark Research Foundation even runs an 'Adopt a Shark' programme to contribute to the great white's preservation. 'The great white is relentlessly persecuted and its declining numbers are becoming of great concern,' he argues. 'There's an urgent need for researchers to find out more about this species so it can survive into the future.'

(Reproduced by permission of John Pinkney.)

Not surprisingly, Rodney never went back to selling insurance. Instead, he turned his hand to professional abalone-diving along the South Australian coast, spending the next 18 years in the very waters which came within a hair's breadth of taking his life. He had three more run-ins with sharks during that time, which he claims is evidence that they are not in great numbers, and that they don't deliberately seek out human food. He also became a champion of the shark's cause, promoting them as highly sophisticated predators who are the absolute rulers of their own territory. He is regarded around the world as *the* shark expert, called upon by filmmakers, documentary crews, aquariums, and anyone who is planning anything to do with sharks and needs advice from the shark's mouth.

Rodney went on to build the world's first underwater observation cage, allowing people to dive safely into the great white's backyard. That development has led to the enormous worldwide interest in not only great whites, but all the potentially dangerous underwater inhabitants of the oceans of the world. Now in his 60s, Rodney still pushes the shark's cause, and still swims in the ocean. He says he would never discourage anyone from enjoying the coastal waters.

'Many more people are killed coming and going from the beach than from shark attacks,' he says. As a survivor, he says he has more a sense of respect for the great white than fear. 'The great white never enters our domain, and we should respect theirs,' he believes.

He is also convinced that sharks have acquired a taste for people and simply do not set out to hunt humans. 'The fact is humans have never been on the shark's menu,' he says. 'It's just that we intrude into their territory.'

Fox says some areas where people go simply present a higher risk than others, and the high risk areas are dotted all around the Australian coast. Swimming, surfing or diving near seal colonies increases the risk of running into a shark, and even waste dumped from ships can attract them. He claims there is no real reason for sharks to cruise metropolitan beaches, and those which are spotted close to busy beaches are generally just passing through. Unless of course they have been attracted by schools of smaller fish, or where bait or fish waste has been dumped into the sea, whether by accident or by fishermen burleying-up the waters to attract their target fish.

Fox is also doubtful about claims over the last few years that shark numbers are on the increase. He believes we just don't have the programmes running to be certain one way or another about what is happening to shark populations. In any event, he is adamant that anyone attacked by a shark will almost certainly not have seen the threat approaching. He didn't see anything until the great white actually locked its jaws onto his torso. But he is very concerned about the 'hysteria' generated over sharks and shark attacks and says he has some regrets about his involvement in the blockbuster movie *Jaws*. 'It frightened people out of the water. It created an unnecessary level of fear,' he said. 'I believe the more we learn about sharks the less fear there will be.'

Spying on the Great White – from Space!

Privacy is a privilege the great white shark can no longer rely upon. For the first time in history, Australian scientists are using an 'eye' in space to monitor a great white's movements.

The breakthrough began in July 2003 when CSIRO researchers hauled a young (100-kilogram) member of the species onto a Victorian fishing boat. After naming their thrashing captive 'Heather', they fitted a satellite transmitter tag to her dorsal fin, then released her.

Every time the still-growing juvenile's fin slices above the water surface it sends a signal to polar-orbiting Argos satellites.

Thanks to data beamed back by these artificial moons, the researchers are already achieving new scientific insights into the great white – a breed whose movements and habits, until now, have largely been swathed in mystery.

Soon after catching Heather off the coast of north-east Tasmania, CSIRO researchers remotely observed her swimming south-west toward Wilson's Promontory in Victoria, before turning around and heading back along the shoreline to Lakes Entrance.

Throughout her time under surveillance she remained at least two nautical miles from land – happily feeding on snapper for many hours of each day.

Numbers of the terrifying but endangered great whites are shrinking every year. The CSIRO team-members hope they can learn enough about the species to be able to help prepare a detailed conservation plan.

The Australian government protects great whites in local waters – and wants a complete ban on international sale of the formidable shark's body parts.

Henri Bource: A Shark Took his Leg – but Not his Spirit

Melbourne journalist Peter Coster still enjoys nothing more than a weekend scuba diving and snorkelling in the waters off some unspoiled section of Australia's coastline. He has been diving for decades, and has seen the best and the worst the ocean is capable of throwing up to surprise human interlopers. A good friend and common diving companion to Coster was Henri Bource, who became something of a legend by not only surviving a white pointer attack, but afterwards going back into the ocean with one good leg and a flipper attached to the stump of his other leg, bitten off by the huge shark.

Henri died of leukemia in his early 60s, more than 30 years after the attack which cost him a leg. Apart from running a business involving cage dives among sharks, he was a very competent musician, and was the resident saxophonist with the 1950s rock band, Gentry. But Coster remembers Henri from their ocean-diving days, and in fact was on the trip in 1964 when his friend was attacked. His compelling stories were published in the *Herald Sun* in October 2000, under the headline 'Big Ben Strikes Terror Under the Sea' (see below).

Big Ben Strikes Terror Under the Sea

In the early 1960s, scuba diving was awesomely adventuresome. We were all young and there were girls and good times. Henri Bource and Irvin Rockman were often together. Irvin drove a two-tone brown Porsche Targa that reminded others, who were older, of corresponding shoes: expensive, flashy, innocently two-faced.

Irvin dived in Noumea when it was considered to be an overseas trip. Henri, then 25, never had that kind of money. But, like Irvin, he had dark good looks and used them. Sometimes, people thought he had the money. Henri played in a band with Johnny Chester. He had a good-looking blonde girlfriend, Jill Ratcliffe. He was just growing up. We were all part of a scuba-diving group introduced to each other by a big traffic cop, Col Johnson. He was sent to Warrnambool from Melbourne, west along the coast near the fishing town of Port Fairy where Henri Bource was to become the most talked about man of the year.

Different aspects of what happened to Henri appealed to people. Some dwelt on the high drama of it all. How the shark 'took' Henri. 'He was taken,' some women were inclined to say. Actually, Henri wasn't 'taken' in the melodramatic parlance of shark attacks. His left leg was taken off at the knee by 'Big Ben', reasonably cleanly when you consider that Big Ben's teeth were as big as the teeth on a wood chipper. Nobody had heard of *Jaws*. Peter Benchley had not written about the giant shark that terrorized a town in New England, America. But Big Ben had left some fishermen from Port Fairy terror-stricken. Big Ben was supposedly a monster shark. A toothy leviathan of the deep who fed hugely on the seal colony on Lady Julia Percy Island, a misnamed, sullen and sharp-edged lump of rock between Port Fairy and Portland, further west.

Big Ben was said to have the scars of fishing boat keels across his back where wide-eyed fishermen gazed in horror at his great dorsal fin. He was said to be 24 feet [7.3 metres], the conversion not yet having been made to metrics in the early 1960s. Big Ben was said to have swallowed great bloody hunks of horsemeat hooked and tied to floating drums. Big Ben towed the drums and the fishing boats, if they had a line attached. It was a better story than *Jaws*, except Big Ben didn't cruise the beaches frightening children and their middle-aged parents. Big Ben merely ate seals – until the day he attacked Henri Bource.

Some of us, who lived in Warrnambool and Port Fairy, had heard of Big Ben. 'Big Col' introduced Henri Bource, Jill Ratcliffe, Irvin Rockman *et al* to other divers from the Warrnambool area to arrange dives. There were some other dives, too. One was on The Pinnacles in Bass Strait, off San Remo. I was 21 and I had one of the first underwater cameras made by Nikon. I took a photograph of Jill Ratcliffe that was published in magazines. She looked good even with a face mask and regulator. So the trip to Lady Julia Percy Island was arranged. A 13.5-metre fishing boat was hired, the *Raemur-K*. Some of us decided that we would make the trip but we would use only scuba. We would not snorkel on the surface in our black wetsuits, imitating seals. The others? Well, they were told. Irvin Rockman wasn't on that trip. Jill Ratcliffe was. I dived with a friend, Geoff

Birtles, who agreed with me that the only time we would spend on the surface was when we surfaced to climb up the ladder on the *Raemur-K*'s side.

It was a clear day. We lay around the deck after the first dive. There was a slight swell. Nothing to disturb the day – except Henri's cries. At first, we weren't quite sure what it was he was saying, if anything intelligible. He was about 80 metres away in the company of two other divers, snorkelling on the surface. Also in the company of some seals they were playing with and in the company, it would seem, of Big Ben.

We did not see Big Ben, the white pointer. There was just Henri Bource on the surface, churning about in ruffled water that had earlier been smooth and heavy.

'The bull seals are attacking him,' someone said. But what bull seal could inflict wounds that poured blood sufficient to cover an area of 20 metres around Henri Bource – so much blood it was still spreading? The boat motor had been started and the *Raemur-K* was now within 30 metres of Henri Bource and his intelligent voice was clearly heard. He was calling on God and his mother – with good reason. The blood was rich red and deep and cloudy on its spreading edges. On the boat there were calls to Christ, too. No more talk of bull seal bites.

The two divers with Henri Bource were some yards [metres] from him. They had spear guns but these would have been toothpicks in the hide of whatever had bitten Henri. Henri Bource called on those on this earth, and beyond, to help him. Jill Ratcliffe was first over into the sea. Geoff Birtles and I were next over the rails and into the red swirl. Under the water, the bubbles from the boat-side plunge cleared and there was a redness. Closer to Bource the red pumped strongly. While holding Bource I was fascinated by the stump of that left leg and its trailing femoral artery, pulsing blood. Fascinated not so much by the chewed end of a human thigh as the missing length of it. The torn neoprene of the wetsuit and the white tendrils of Henri Bource's leg were nothing compared with the disappearance of the limb itself.

Topside on the *Raemur-K*, hands were reaching down. Through his face mask, Henri Bource's face was devoid of blood. The blood had pumped away. His face seemed already lifeless, pumped dry leaving a mask beneath the mask. The swell lifted the hull of the *Raemur-K* over us. Only a foot thrust against the side prevented it smashing us senseless. A rubber engine breathing pipe gave a handhold and enough leverage to lift Bource's body to the hands above. Underneath the boat, blood still clouded. Is it possible there can be so much?

Looking back from the boat the blood trailed away. Henri Bource is lying on the deck, lying as he was pulled aboard. Of those aboard, one is a male nurse who knows that to move him could induce secondary shock and surely kill him. Surely, he is dead? A hand pinches the still-pumping femoral artery. A rubber is cut from a spear-gun and used as a tourniquet. We are to learn that Bource has lost 2.8 litres of the 6.2 litres of blood carried in his body. Henri Bource is silent, as are most others on the boat. Someone is weeping on the stern. Big Col is heaving into the sea. What does it matter? The rubber tourniquet is loosened and retied. Surely there can be no more blood to seep from him?

The radio on board seems to raise no-one until a voice from Apollo Bay down the coast tells us that our emergency call has been repeated to the police and the Warrnambool Base Hospital is ready to help Henri Bource and an ambulance is waiting back at Port Fairy. Can Henri Bource live until the *Raemur-K* returns to berth? We decide he cannot. An old man, the father of the skipper, steps from the wheelhouse and we run at full speed over shoals he knows over a lifetime at sea. We see the coral heads glide by beneath the keel and we reach Port Fairy and he is still alive. There are hundreds of the fascinated upon the wharf. They look as a doctor comes aboard with plasma. And so it went on.

Henri Bource recovered remarkably quickly, a tribute to his youth and fitness and that he spent as much time keeping himself healthy as riding in Irvin Rockman's two-tone brown Porsche, the one that looked like the fancy shoe. He was a celebrity and radio stations played the songs he recorded with Johnny Chester.

He continued diving after he recovered. He tied a swim fin to the stump and manoeuvred a heavy camera years later when we swam down to the wreck of the *Loch Ard*, a square rigger which hit a reef along the Victorian Shipwreck Coast. He shot a film, *Savage Shadows*, which told the story of how he survived the Lady Julia Percy Island attack, and later formed his own commercial diving team which worked on the Bass Strait gas fields. He said he did not hate sharks. 'It was doing what sharks do,' he always said.

Some who were involved in the attack went back aboard the *Raemur-K* for the re-enactment. As with many films, the actors involved let everyone know they knew more about what happened than anyone who happened to be there. The re-enactment was filmed in a bay near Port Fairy, far away from Lady Julia Percy Island. The protagonist, Big Ben, was in everyone's mind but he was not in the water, at least not there that day. But I have felt his presence since.

Some of us later tried to catch a white pointer off Lady Julia Percy Island, because that is surely what the shark that attacked Henri was. I remember sitting in a chair on the stern of a game-fishing boat off the island. This was not a revenge mission. It was just an attempt to catch a shark on rod and reel. We had been off the island for hours, lacing the water with buckets of blood and offal, but there hadn't been any bites.

I was close to dozing in the chair, hand gripping the big-game rod and reel when a voice beside me hissed: 'It's moving. It's moving!' The bait, a lump of bloody meat hanging on a hook that could have suspended a steer's carcass, was moving, but slowly, so slowly that the slick water was rippling as the thick line cut through it. Slowly, I raised the bait. The ripples around the line stopped. Slowly the line started moving through the water again.

'It's nosing it,' came a whisper from someone else. 'It's seeing if it's safe to eat.' Perhaps the shark might hear us if we spoke too loudly? The line then started moving quickly through the water, actually cutting its own little wake. There was a deep swirl, as if something big was moving below. A vortex ringed the surface. Then it was gone.

Several things were learned from these experiences: a white pointer was almost certainly the shark that attacked Henri and it was surely a white pointer that was carefully nosing the bait below the boat. And it was most likely a great white that attacked Rodney Fox, a South Australian diver, in 1963 [see page 102]. Fox needed 462 stitches in his ravaged body. 'The shark spat me out, didn't he,' said Fox, who ran shark-cage dives in Spencer Gulf. 'I was too bony for him.' Fox saw the shark come back for him a second time. In Henri's case, it was once. The shark took his leg and was gone. Or it might have been circling as we pushed Henri up against the side of the boat so others could pull him aboard. There was something blurred on the periphery of vision. That memory came back to me a few years later when a big hammerhead circled another diver and me as we were ascending in open water in the Sea of Cortez in Mexico. The shark was about four metres in length. It faded in and out of our vision.

The first time it circled I wasn't sure if it was a shark – or anything at all. It circled twice more, in and out of vision, then faded away. Benchley had written *Jaws* by then, and I often remember the music. Hammerheads can be dangerous, but are usually easily frightened. A burst of bubbles will almost always turn them. Great white sharks are the ambushers. Of the attacks on divers and surfers, usually the first sign of their presence is when they attack. Some divers say they will drift away if their instincts tell them they have been seen. But they sometimes press home an attack. Abalone divers have told how white pointers have kept them holed up among rocks for hours.

Not all sharks are 'man-eaters', just as not all swimmers are 'taken' by sharks. Sometimes they are bitten and survive. Sometimes not. We are frightened of sharks because we know that when we are in the sea we are in a realm where the white pointer is at the top of the food chain. They prefer seals, but sometimes humans will do.

Benchley's book, *Jaws*, published in the 1970s, made sharks our favourite nightmare. The monster white pointer still terrifies children when it raises its great body out of the water several times a day at Universal Studios, where the movie *Jaws* was made. The shark in *Jaws* was vengeful. Remember how it finally ate Robert Shaw, who was trying to kill it?

Benchley, who has been on shark-cage dives with Fox in South Australia and with *National Geographic* photographer David Doubilet off South Africa, has since learned a lot about sharks. They were together a few months ago off Gansbaai on the South African coast when they saw great whites bursting from the water while chasing prey. Their acrobatics were similar to a marlin after it has taken the hook or whales when they breach and blow. White pointers are big, perhaps up to six metres in length and weighing more than a tonne. It takes an incredible amount of energy to lift that much weight from the water.

Benchley described it as a rush from the dark, an explosion at the surface, a balletic somersault, a splash. Fox gasped when he saw it. 'The violence! My Lord, the violence.' This is why we remember shark attacks.

In 2000 the Australian government tried to have sharks declared an endangered species at the Convention on International Trade in Endangered Species (CITES) in Nairobi. Perhaps no-one liked sharks as much as Australians. The motion was defeated though Australia has its own laws to protect white pointers. Sharks such as white pointers are part of the food chain. They just happen to be at the top. Together with tiger sharks and whalers, they are responsible for an average of less than one death a year in Australia. But killing these magnificent predators in response to an attack will achieve nothing. They are doing what they have done for at least 200 million years.

(Reproduced by permission of Peter Coster and The Herald and Weekly Times.)

Gary 'Whitebait' White: 'Luckiest Man Alive'

Kilcunda on Victoria's south-east coast is a great drawcard for fishermen and surfers. Coming from Wonthaggi or Phillip Island, tourists are treated to a stunning view as they climb towards the top of Black Head. Waves rush in from Bass Strait to crash headlong onto the cliffs and beaches that make up one of the most picturesque spots on the whole Victorian coast, and the Powlett River empties itself over the beach and into the strait.

The Killy Pub is a must for passing holiday-makers to break their journey, and a regular stop-off point for groups of motorbike fans out for a club ride-day. But sharks are no respecters of scenery, nor do they care that a fisherman or surfer might be feeling at one with the world as they go about their chosen recreation on and in the water. It was a shark that put Gary White of Wonthaggi into local folklore one day late in November, 1989. Gary survived to tell the tale, and to be dubbed with the nickname to which he still answers.

And while the scarring may have faded, his memories are still fresh. After the attack Gary went to a tattooist, and on his right shoulder, until the day he dies and some time afterwards, he'll carry the picture of a great white, baring its teeth. Below the shark is the word 'Kilcunda' and the date, permanently etched in his memory as well as on his skin: 22–11–89.

Three months after being attacked Gary went back into the water, with a new surfboard, but also with some lingering fear he had to overcome. His old surfing mates welcomed him back onto the waves, and immediately dubbed him 'Whitebait', his nickname from that day on.

Gary White was 32 when he became part of surfing legend. The shark that attacked him in the water at Kilcunda was later estimated by shark hunter Vic Hislop to have been six metres long. The great white shark bit his surfboard in half with one crunching motion of its jaws, and dragged Gary under the water. As it bit down on the board, however, it caught Gary by the leg, pulling him along for eight or nine metres, before finding the fibreglass and foam of the surfboard not to its liking and spitting it out, and spitting Gary out along with it. When he surfaced his surfing mate, Greg 'Snapper' Swift, was able to grab him and drag him back to shore.

The rushed trip to Wonthaggi Hospital was the longest 14 kilometres of Gary's life. Once there he discovered how unbelievably lucky he had been. His only legacy was a gash in his left leg which needed 27 stitches. Given the size of the great white which attacked him, 'Kilcunda 22–11–89' should have been on his gravestone instead of his shoulder. At the Killy Pub, in Wonthaggi, and at surf beaches all along the coast, long-term residents and surfers still wonder how Gary managed to survive that day. Some also wonder how he could face going back into the water afterwards.

It took three months, but Gary did get back on a surfboard and did start catching waves again at Kilcunda Beach. A builder by trade, he had been surfing for 16 years and even while in the hospital he intended to get back into the water. But the comeback was not without difficulty, and even now he clearly recalls the attack, and still has a shiver of apprehension every so often.

'Surfing is never going to be what it used to be for me. When I'm in the water it'll always be in the back of my mind, it is always there,' he said. 'I went to the beach three times but didn't go in.' Finally however, he did. 'I just went out and surfed. I didn't think about it … I was a bit nervous when I got to the beach, but the waves were pumping,' he said.

In launching a comeback, he was also lucky to have the support of his surfing mates. Two friends organized a big party, attended by locals and surfers from far and wide, and charged an entrance fee. The money raised got Gary a new surfboard, but the whole occasion was also a great help in enabling him to get his mental state sorted out and avoid any long-lasting fear which would have made it impossible for him to go anywhere near the ocean. When he resumed surfing, he tried to push shark phobia out of his mind. And while he's done that successfully, he can still recall instantly every second of the attack.

At the time, he described himself as 'the luckiest man alive'. He recalls being about 100 metres offshore when the shark struck.

'It came right up next to me and swam past,' Gary said.

124

'It took a few seconds to go past and I just watched it. I was thinking, God, I'm going to get eaten. I'm the main course. It just hit me and dragged me underwater.'

Gary's surfing mate, Greg 'Snapper' Swift, said the whole patch of water was 'thrashing'.

'Gary burst out of the water and two pieces of surfboard flew out either side of him,' Greg said. 'He was just screaming – it was real *Jaws* stuff.' Amazingly several of the group Gary was surfing with actually saw the shark as they were in the water, but because none had ever seen a great white at Kilcunda before, they put the mysterious dark shape lurking under the water down as a dolphin.

Another of Gary's friends, Craig Lindsay, said a group of surfers had gone to Kilcunda Beach to make the most of a perfect surfing day. 'I got out of the water just before he was attacked by the shark,' Craig said. 'None of us knew what had happened until he struggled out of the water.

'He seemed to be in some kind of trouble and we thought he must have busted a leg or something, and then he called out for us to give him a hand up the hill. He told us he'd been attacked by a shark. We couldn't believe it. He was in a fair bit of pain, but he kept it together really well.'

At the time Gary was married with two young girls aged three and eight months. The help of the community and his boss was just as important as the support of his surfer mates in leading him towards recovery, although he said his leg has never been quite the same.

'Physically, the leg will never be the same as it was' he said. 'The way I look at it, I'm lucky to have it.' Apart from the scar, the tattoo, general shark phobia and often a reluctance to surf at Kilcunda, there is another legacy of his run in with the great white. 'I'll never surf by myself again. I'll always surf with mates.'

Two Divers who Survived a Brush with White Death

*T*wo South Australian divers have done battle with the white death, one more than 40 years ago and the other 20 years ago, and have lived to tell their stories. *Adelaide Advertiser* feature writer Peter Hackett spoke with both men. Hackett's report is reproduced below:

The First Survivor: Brian Rodger

It's the jaws that Brian Rodger remembers. Those massive, gaping jaws, awesome white teeth flashing through the water. Homing in on him. No escape.

'There is no pain involved whatsoever. Pain is not an issue,' said Rodger, one of the few people in the world to survive the attack of a great white shark, also known as a white pointer. 'You just don't have time to think about that. It was like a stifled scream – to find that you are confronting the worst thing you could ever imagine.'

On a warm afternoon in 1961, when Rodger was just 21 years old, his life almost came to a savage end. He was spearfishing one afternoon off the reef at Aldinga, a popular diving spot on the Gulf St Vincent south of Adelaide, when his worst nightmare surged from the deep.

'I was taking part in a spearfishing competition,' he

said. 'I had been in the water about four hours and I was way out, about one kilometre. I had all the fish I could pick up and I was heading back to shore.

'Suddenly, without warning, I felt something grab on to my left leg. I didn't get any perception of cutting, no real feeling of pain. I looked around and I saw this huge head clamped on to my leg. It was a shark. I remember thinking, I will have to be bloody lucky to get out of this.'

Rodger had been attacked from behind by a four-metre white pointer. He didn't see it coming. There was no warning and there was nowhere to hide. He was alone and with no help in sight. The sea water around him began to turn red. It was his blood, his life flowing away.

'I turned around and went for its eyes,' he said. 'But my fist went straight into its mouth. My wrist was shredded to the bone. It then did what sharks seem to do a lot. It released me and went off, heading out in an arc of about 15 metres.'

Just for a moment, Rodger thought he was safe. His body was charged with adrenaline but he was bleeding to death. And then he saw that deadly dorsal fin and it was targeting him, striking back for the final crunch, to finish him off. This, he thought, must be how his short life was going to end.

'When it came back at me I managed to get my spear-gun pointed up and, fortunately, it was loaded. I hit it just behind the eye,' Rodger said. 'It shook the spear out of its head and took off. I was floating in the water. I remember there was a lot of blood around.'

It had seemed like hours but the attack had lasted only

a few minutes. Rodger was exhausted, still a long way from the safety of the beach, and he could feel his lifeblood draining away. 'I was very weak,' he said, 'but I realized that I could still swim. I could see my arm and leg were ripped open. The wetsuit helped. I took the rubber from my spear gun and used it as a tourniquet on my leg. Using my right thumb, I clamped the blood pressure under my arm. I was still about one kilometre from shore. About 100 metres from shore, I began yelling, "Shark! Shark!" And then someone came to help me.'

What went through his mind when he realized he was being attacked and savaged by a shark?

'It was like the turning point – between living and dying,' said Rodger. You find out an awful lot about yourself, about your survival instincts. I had never been that close to a shark before and I soon realized that this was a very big shark – and very capable of killing me. Just after the attack, I didn't expect to live. When it first attacked, I was in survival mode. When it came back, I went into fighting mode.'

From the wounds inflicted, it was estimated that the shark had jaws measuring 58 centimetres. It took about 400 stitches to patch up the massive mutilation and today, 39 years later, the scars of Rodger's terrifying encounter are still clearly visible. His near-death experience did not turn him away from the water. Brian Rodger continued to go spearfishing and for about ten years worked as a professional abalone diver in South Australian waters.

'I still dive recreationally,' he said, 'but I don't like the gulf [Gulf St Vincent] much. The water is a bit dirty and there is not a lot for sharks to feed on – so they are more likely to go for you. I think we have now become part of their food chain. We have interfered with the food chain and we are now part of it. I don't have a silly fear about it. You know the risk is there. It's a calculated risk. There are sharks – and there are white pointers. The white pointer is particularly well designed to eat something our size.'

Reflecting on the attack, Rodger said: 'For all the terror of it, it's a kind of exhilarating experience. It's a very terrifying experience but it adds a bit of lust to your life.' Not many people have come face to face with a white pointer shark, looked it in the eye, and come away to tell the story …

The Second Survivor: Neil Williams

Neil Williams was recalling his intimate encounter with the supreme killer of the southern oceans. It was the day before Christmas 1983 and the professional abalone diver had headed out with a mate for one last haul for the year. They went to South Neptune Island, about 70 kilometres south of Port Lincoln in South Australia. The Neptune Island group was well-known as a seal colony and as the territory of the great white shark. It was used as a location in the filming of the thriller *Jaws*.

'I dived down about 200 metres offshore, in about 30 metres of water,' Williams recalled. 'I had picked up about half a bag of abalone and I was swimming toward the reef. I turned around and there it was. It was about 15 metres away. It turned and swam towards me. It stopped right in front of me. Its snout was only about 45 centimetres from my face mask and it was just staring at me.

'Then it opened its huge jaws and I realized it was going to eat me. All I could see was this huge, gaping mouth with teeth all around it. The jaws were going in and out. It lifted its nose and all I could see was teeth.'

And what went through his mind when he realized he was about to die a most gruesome death in the jaws of a shark?

'I just thought, this is it, my time is up,' he said. 'After all these years of diving, I am going to go out this way. It's not a feeling that you ever forget.'

In one final, desperate act of survival, Williams grabbed his bag of abalone and thrust it into the jaws of the monster that was about to devour him. 'I thrust the bag into its mouth. It all happened in a matter of seconds,' he said.

'It was biting at the bag but still coming at me. It pushed right over the top of me and as it went by, I tried to push it away. But it must have been at least 3.6 metres long. When I pushed the bag into its mouth my hand caught on its teeth. I was bleeding and I could see that I was pretty badly cut up. But I wasn't worried about that. I was trying to stay alive, I wasn't worried about losing a couple of fingers.'

With blood streaming from his wounds, Williams headed for the seabed, considered by divers to be the safest ground. 'All the time I was looking around for the shark and thinking, my God, I am still alive. I didn't want to leave the bottom because once you do that you are very vulnerable,' he said. 'I was looking for somewhere to hide. The shark circled and came back at me several times and I thought, this is it, it's going to take me this time.'

With his back jammed against a rock, at one point it came so close that 'it brushed against me', Williams said. He was also concerned that the shark might bite and sever his air hose, which would force him to free-float to the surface, making him a very easy target.

'There was blood flowing from my hand. I was trying to clamp the wound with my other hand, because I knew the shark would pick up on all the blood.'

Williams moved slowly across the sea floor, heading towards the shoreline. Eventually, he looked up and saw the bottom of his boat. At about 100 metres from shore, in 15 metres of water, he inflated his abalone 'parachute' and rode up with it to the surface.

'As I hit the surface, I had this vision of the shark following me up,' he said. 'If it follows you up, it's going to take your legs off. But my mate pulled me into the boat. I just fell down, exhausted and thought, I am alive. If I hadn't had that bag of abalone, that shark certainly would have taken me.'

Williams, now 64, continued to operate an abalone business out of Port Lincoln and did some of the diving. Neptune Island was recognized as the home of the great white and, while abalone divers still worked the area, Williams said, 'Now they only go down there with cages, because it's just too dangerous.'

There were also fears that the prevalence of film crews and thrill-seeking recreational divers feeding sharks had caused the great white to focus much more on wetsuits. It had, quite simply, put something new on its menu.

'They are very unpredictable, more so than any other

shark I know,' said Williams, who had been abalone diving for 36 years. 'You never know what they're going to do and if you go into their territory, you're fair game. There is no escape, there is nowhere to run. You know that if you run into a white pointer you are in big trouble. It's the moment of truth.'

Abalone divers had learnt to live with and respect the great white, 'but the general philosophy is, you won't see the one that gets you'.

Neil Williams and the great white shark shared the same territory but Williams said he knew exactly where he stood in the food chain. 'I should have been dead and I'm not,' he said. 'So every day now is a bonus for me. Going through what I went through with that shark certainly changes your attitude to life.'

(Reproduced by permission of Peter Hackett and The Herald and Weekly Times.)

A Close Encounter

Despite the old joke, not even lawyers are immune from a shark attack. A former champion footballer with Melbourne's St Kilda club, Brian Sierakowski, and a friend had a very near miss off Perth's suburban Cottesloe Beach.

Mr Sierakowski, a barrister, and his plastic surgeon friend, Doctor Barney Hanrahan, were paddling their double surf-ski about 6.45am on 29 October 1997 when a five-metre white pointer decided to investigate. Afterwards he said the shark came in with no warning whatsoever.

The first indication either man had that something was seriously wrong with their morning paddle was when a huge set of jaws clamped down on the surf-ski, only 30 centimetres from Mr Sierakowski's feet. In media interviews afterwards the former football champion, who played in St Kilda's 1966 premiership team, said he was thinking there was absolutely nothing he could do.

'This is too big for me, I can't fight this, it's too big a beast,' he told one interviewer. He said the great white just kept biting down on the surf-ski, thrashing about and its shoulder was hitting him in he face. The shark eventually pulled away with a mouthful of fibreglass and foam, but the troubles weren't over for the barrister and the plastic surgeon. The surf-ski was sinking with water getting inside the shell through the great hole torn in it by the beast's teeth. Both men just lay flat on the surf-ski, their bodies entirely out of the water, praying for help to arrive.

Other paddlers out that morning at Cottesloe came to their aid. Another barrister, Malcolm McCusker, his wife Diane and another friend, Milton Barker, were able to get a grip on the damaged and sinking ski and drag it to shore. Two hours later, Brian Sierakowski drove himself to work after heading home for a shower and some minor patch-up work on facial and leg abrasions caused by the rough skin of the one that nearly got him. He was actually back in the water at Cottesloe the next day.

But three years later stark reality caught up with the barrister, almost as if he had a delayed reaction. In November 2000, when Ken Crew was taken by a white pointer at the same beach, Brian Sierakowski had a serious re-think.

His mood – like that of many others who called North Cottesloe their second home – quickly switched from the bravado and good humour which surrounded his escape three years earlier. After Ken Crew's death the burly former champion footballer and lawyer could barely look at the water. He became convinced the great white which killed Mr Crew was still lurking off Cottesloe, and until he could be persuaded it had moved on he was not going back in the water.

Mr Sierakowski said he didn't hesitate getting back on a surf-ski after his scrape three years ago. 'I was back in the water next morning,' he said. But after the fatal attack on Ken Crew and the injuries suffered by another friend, Dirk Avery, who tried to help Mr Crew, Sierakowski acknowledged the tragedy had struck a deep fear into the hearts of all who normally swam there.

'Now I can't face the water because I know in my guts it's still out there. I had taken the view that I was a little bit invincible but knowing what I now know … my gut aches,' he said. 'Our incident turned out to be a lucky and miraculous escape and we made levity of it. This tragedy brought home how fine that line is.

'Those of us who enjoy this lifestyle, that's many thousands, are suddenly faced with a very serious predicament, because our beaches aren't safe,' he said. 'They are wonderful, clean, pristine places, but they are not safe from sharks. This shark is a killer shark. The best they could do is get rid of it. Firstly, it has killed, and secondly, there is nothing to say it isn't the same shark which attacked us.'

He said the food chain in the waters off Perth's popular beaches had changed since he was attacked. 'We've noticed in the morning when we are paddling, there is a lot more fish activity. There are big chopper tailor and seals around, and when there is a seal you have got to be conscious of the fact there is a shark around.'

Mr Sierakowski was staggered by the thought that a 4.5-metre white pointer – possibly weighing 1.5 tonnes – would virtually beach itself in its attack on Dirk Avery as he was trying to help Ken Crew out of the water. He believes it could even be the same one that attacked him.

Short Shark Tales

An Attack in Sydney Harbour

One of the last places anyone would expect a shark attack would be way up in Sydney Harbour, near the Leichardt Rowing Club. But somebody forgot to tell the shark that attacked Andree Mocsari, 49, that it wasn't supposed to be that far from the open ocean.

Andree had just put her $9,000 carbon-fibre scull in the water and was about 100 metres from the clubhouse. She'd just started her daily 12-kilometre ritual, which she had been carrying out for six years, when the scull was hit from behind, as if by an express train. It was 6.15am on 3 February 1997, and visibility was far from perfect.

Andree was somersaulted from the boat by the force of the impact, straight into the water. She said she didn't realize it was a shark for a few seconds, thinking she may have hit a floating log, but when she saw the ominous dark shape in the water and 50 centimetres or so of the shark's back break the surface, she knew only too well what had happened.

'I was flailing the water and I was terrified he was going to come back and get me,' she said on shore afterwards. Her fellow rowers were not a lot of immediate help. They thought she'd just fallen into the water, and were having a laugh at her expense, also taking their time rowing across to help her back into the scull.

They soon changed their tune once everyone was back on shore. Inspecting the stern of the lightweight but thankfully enormously strong carbon fibre hull they found five clear gouges. Mute evidence that Andree was indeed telling the truth, and ample explanation for the bad case of the shakes she was going through.

Mako Mayhem

Fishermen have been known to stretch the truth back at the bar of the local pub, or around the campfire, but the story Ian Richardson tells of a fishing trip after a few flathead is unbelievable but true, or truly unbelievable.

He and his girlfriend, Gail Young, had launched their boat at Lewisham, not far off the road between Hobart and Port Arthur, on 21 February 1997. They were fishing the waters of Frederick Henry Bay when something jumped out of the water nearby. At first they thought their luck was in and they were going to have a close-up look at some dolphins.

The pair quickly realized it was a mako shark, and it wasn't alone. The two sharks began circling the boat, eyeing off the fish Ian and Gail had already caught. They were relatively small makos, a bit under two metres, so Ian and Gail did what any keen fishermen would and tried to hook one up. Ian said he got one, but it just snapped the line.

That's when the fun started. One of the makos leapt

from the water, straight into the small boat, shirt-fronting Ian as it flew through the air and knocking Gail over as well. The unwelcome visitor thrashed around in the front of the boat for 20 minutes while the flathead seekers screamed, and tried to dodge its flailing tail.

Eventually the mako lay still in the front of the boat, while Ian and Gail fired up the motor and headed ashore, driving from as far back in the boat as they could.

'Miracle Wave' Saves Schoolteacher

Surfers need to be a hardy lot. Every time they take to the water they pit themselves against two of nature's most irresistible forces. They go up against the mindless, changeable power of the ocean, which they can see and to some extent, understand, but also against the implacable and totally predatory sharks which live in that ocean, which they rarely see, and if they do it almost always means trouble.

Mark Butler didn't see the shark which all but tore his leg from his body when it struck him from below at Brooms Head Beach on the New South Wales north coast on 4 February 2001. The schoolteacher from Yamba was paddling his board only 80 metres from shore when razor sharp teeth closed on his left leg in a vice-like grip.

The shark shook him, tearing a huge slab of muscle out of his left thigh, and then let go. Gushing blood, Mark began paddling his board towards shore, and then caught what he described as a 'miracle wave' which deposited him at the water's edge.

Driven only by thoughts of his three children and the certain knowledge he had mere minutes to live if he didn't get help, he used the legrope of his surfboard as a makeshift tourniquet. It slowed the bleeding marginally; there was too much damage to the thigh for any sort of tourniquet to be truly effective.

The beach was deserted when he made shore, but holding the wound together as best he could Mark climbed a sand dune and staggered almost 500 metres to get help. In the water Mark feared the shark would come back to finish him off, and on the sand he was convinced he would die from loss of blood.

Neither happened but he was lapsing in and out of consciousness before medical help arrived. Once in hospital surgeons battled for more than 90 minutes to get life-saving blood transfusions into Mark, and to rejoin what they could of the severed blood vessels and muscle tissue. Mark Butler survived the attack, and thanks to his presence of mind and determination gave doctors the chance they needed to save his leg and his life.

Surfer Survives a Bronze Whaler Attack

Surf-shop proprietor, Richard Ellis, 40, had a run-in with a bronze whaler about 10am on 3 April 2001 while surfing at the mouth of the Nambucca River on the New South Wales north coast. He was extraordinarily lucky, losing a chunk of calf muscle but managing to stay on his surfboard.

In shock, but with enormous presence of mind, he caught the next wave into shore, getting out of the area of bloodied water, and possibly leaving the whaler swimming around in circles, looking for the lunch that got away. Once ashore, Richard and other surfers tied the leg rope from his board around his leg as a tourniquet, and with the blood loss minimized his friends carried him across Shelley Beach and over the dunes to the carpark.

He was taken to an ambulance depot a few kilometres away and then rushed to hospital, conscious all the time. Richard said afterwards he had no idea the shark was lining him up, but he did recall seeing dolphins, which are fairly common in the area, milling together moments before the attack.

A Gummy Goes to Hospital

In one bizarre encounter, a shark was taken to hospital, along with its victim. The gentle little gummy shark, a favourite with anglers because they provide a good feed after a good fight and virtually no danger, is generally regarded as completely harmless. But on 9 April 2001, one at Sydney's Bronte Beach must have been having a very bad day when it attached itself to a swimmer's arm, and wouldn't let go.

The gummy doesn't have teeth as we know them. They have flattened bony plates, used for crushing shellfish and crustaceans like crabs. They can grow to 1.7 metres in length, but are usually 1–1.2 metres only, weighing in at around five kilograms. All in all, pretty harmless and much favoured for the flake fillet market.

But the swimmer at Bronte just struck one at the wrong

time. It wouldn't let go, and the man swam ashore with the gummy clinging to his arm. Lifesavers on the beach had to run a filletting knife across its throat to make it let go

Both swimmer and shark were taken to hospital, the swimmer mainly for a quick check-over and a tetanus shot, and the shark? Well, no-one is too sure why the fish went.

Shark Bites Hole through Surfboard

Another surfer, Mick Valentine, 37, had his near death experience on the New South Wales central coast off Noraville, near Toukley. He'd been surfing for several hours without mishap and certainly without even sighting a shark, large or small.

It was getting on to dusk, about 5.45pm on 2 May 2001, when Mick's surfboard was hit very hard from the side and shoved several metres sideways across the water. Mick was hurled into the water, and when he surfaced he saw his board had a hole bitten right through it.

Until that terrifying split second of realization, he didn't know he'd been the target of a shark. He realized then just how close he had come. The 30-centimetre gash across his chest, pouring blood into the water, kicked him into action. Mick grabbed what was left of his board and paddled as hard as he could for shore, with all sorts of mental pictures going through his mind.

'I thought I was dead. I thought I was going to die right there and then,' he said afterwards. 'I just didn't stop paddling until I reached the sand.'

Still bleeding heavily, he was helped up the sand by a

fellow surfer and taken to Wyong Hospital, where the gash, which could so easily have been fatal, was stitched up.

Dangers Lurking in Murky Waters ...

Paul McNamara, 35, now knows better, but he virtually set himself up for a shark attack on 9 February 2002. Kayaking in the Parramatta River at dusk, the water warm and murky, the sky overcast, and the swirling of his paddle going through the water, he was a made-to-order shark attractor. Paul was paddling near Carbarita Marina when a two-metre bull shark launched itself at the stern of his kayak and took a grip on it. The whaler shook the kayak, flinging

Paul into the air and then into the water. Disoriented, he looked across and saw the fin and back of the shark at the rear of his damaged kayak, which was still floating a couple of metres away.

He spotted a red-and-white painted wooden channel marker but as he began swimming towards it he also saw the shark beginning to circle him. Then without warning it cannoned into his chest, winding him and forcing him underwater, but not biting.

Paul managed to reach the channel marker and clamber up it enough to get most of his body out of the water, but the next few minutes seemed like a lifetime as he imagined the shark lining up the bits still in the water – his buttocks – for another attack.

He was rescued from his precarious perch by a passing boat and taken ashore. His only injuries were some lacerations on his legs, caused by his clamber up the channel marker, not the teeth nor skin of the whaler that attacked him.

It wasn't much comfort to Paul, but afterwards a shark expert from Taronga Zoo, John West, said bull sharks were common in Sydney Harbour during summer. They are very fond of hanging around river mouths where the water is often warm and a bit murky, waiting for fish being washed downstream when the tide is turning to run out.

He said they were also inquisitive, and given the water and weather conditions at the time this one was probably just testing the kayak with its mouth, to see if it was edible.

The Attack of the Dead Shark

Sometimes there is a funny side to a shark attack where survival, instead of bringing glory and awe, brings embarrassment. Long-time Tasmanian fisherman Terry Horton lived not only to tell the tale, but also to cop the ribbing of his mates when he was bitten by a 120-kilogram mako shark on 17 February 2002.

Terry and a friend had been out in Terry's 11-metre boat on a successful day's fishing. The friend had hooked up on the mako, and they towed it back to the jetty at Eaglehawk Neck. As they dragged their trophy up onto the jetty, it slipped through Terry's hands, and one razor-sharp tooth sliced cleanly through his trousers and slashed across his knee down to the bone.

Unwilling at first to admit he'd been mauled by a dead shark, Terry tried to ignore the wound, but a gumboot full of blood soon persuaded him something ought to be done. An overnight stay in hospital and ten stitches later he was up and about again – in fact he was out fishing again the next day.

Terry said it was the first time, and he hoped it would be the last, he'd been bitten by a shark, let alone a dead one.

Exploding Sharks Topple a Tourist

It was the most terrifying day in Perth shop assistant Hazel Swinden's life.

While strolling through the Sydney Aquarium at Darling Harbour on 20 February 1997, holidaying Hazel suddenly heard a sharp 'CRACK' as a tank exploded.

Seconds later she was showered with sharks. Not to speak of 2.5 tonnes of water and flying fragments of glass.

Hazel was one of four people taken to hospital after they were hit by a 'wall of water' populated by seven thrashing white-and-black-tipped reef sharks. The unexpected encounter sent Hazel skidding across the floor with the sharks flapping around her.

'I thought I was dying … I thought I was dead,' she said, when her compensation case came before the New South Wales District Court six years later (August 2003).

Hazel's lawyer John Pender told the court that she had been taken to Royal Prince Alfred Hospital where she had surgery and stayed for four days. She had suffered a severed tendon in her left ankle – and multiple cuts and bruises, sustained when she was slammed against a wall during the flood. The case was still being heard as this book went to press.

Living With Sharks

The Anti-protection View

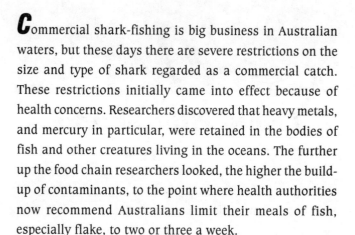

Commercial shark-fishing is big business in Australian waters, but these days there are severe restrictions on the size and type of shark regarded as a commercial catch. These restrictions initially came into effect because of health concerns. Researchers discovered that heavy metals, and mercury in particular, were retained in the bodies of fish and other creatures living in the oceans. The further up the food chain researchers looked, the higher the build-up of contaminants, to the point where health authorities now recommend Australians limit their meals of fish, especially flake, to two or three a week.

Health concerns aside, modern technology has enabled us to venture into the world of the shark. Today we know more than ever before about the denizens of the deep, and the more spectacular of the sharks have become a favourite with conservationists – to the point where now great whites are a totally protected species in Australian waters.

This has not been achieved without serious argument. One of the most vociferous proponents of protection has been Rodney Fox, attack survivor (see page 102), and his equally loud opponent in the argument has been Vic Hislop, who has made a very good living out of hunting, catching and displaying great whites.

If anyone can lay claim to the title Great White Hunter, it is Vic Hislop. The Hislop shark shows in Queensland attract tens of thousands of visitors each year, and until the sharks became protected, Hislop would turn up regularly, armed for the hunt, whenever and wherever a great white, or any other shark for that matter, attacked a human being.

He has been arguing for decades that sharks are a danger to humans, that we are the rulers of the planet and are entitled to go where we like, including their domain, with impunity.

Some of his arguments may sound extreme, some may smack of conspiracy theories, and they may be out of touch with the times, but they are honestly-held views. In the pursuit of his beliefs he has run foul of the law several times, and has had his shark-hunting gear confiscated and has been convicted of offences.

The Conspiracy Theory

Hislop has accused government bureaucrats of whitewashing the dangers posed by killer sharks in favour of their protectionist policies. Banned from shark-catching, initially in South Australia and Victoria, and now nationally, he has claimed that a conspiracy between department of Fisheries officials, filmmakers who use sharks as subjects, and a mixed bag of 'radical greenies stirred up by lies' has effectively suppressed the truth about great whites and their habits.

Hislop has 30 years experience hunting sharks. He

has, however, been convinced for years there existed a 'Get-Hislop' campaign, motivated by personal greed, political power-broking and what he termed misguided greenie activists. He claimed he was targeted in an effort to drive him out of the water and force him to close his two shark shows in Queensland. Without naming anyone, he has claimed certain people wanted him out of the way so they could continue to film sharks in feeding frenzies, lower celebrities in steel cages into shark-filled waters and promote killer sharks as 'misunderstood creatures that won't harm you if you leave them alone'.

That's a belief Hislop has always labelled as absolute rubbish. According to him the activities in support of leaving sharks alone have actually increased the danger to humans by teaching them to include us in their food chain.

'Sharks will eat anything in their food chain,' he says. 'Humans once had a slight chance to escape because the shark would hesitate before attacking because we aren't his natural food. Now, because of filmmaking in recent years, some sharks are familiar with our shape and that natural hesitation has been removed from their behaviour. Those same filmmakers are known to stuff wetsuits with fish, put the human shapes on surfboards, berley-up the water with tuna oil and blood, and then film the big whites coming in and tearing the dummy and board to pieces.

'These sharks then patrol our beaches and, if they see a similar target, naturally they will attack. There have been 12 surfboard attacks in Australia in the past two years – some would have been attacks by these same sharks trained by humans.' Hislop claims the filmmakers have 'fooled the poor old radical conservationists into pressuring politicians' to have him banned from shark-hunting. 'There's a lot of money involved here and the issue has nothing to do with conservation. The true reason is profit and I stand in their way, but I can't stand back and let them get away with it,' he said.

In November 1987, Hislop caught the biggest great white ever landed up to that time – a 2.5 tonne monster hooked off Phillip Island, near Melbourne. Hislop's bureaucratic battle then geared-up in earnest. He had a ten-day permit to fish for sharks but ran foul of the system when he landed the great white. Although hundreds of spectators applauded him on the beach, the shark hunter's elation was short-lived. Joan Kirner, then the Victorian Conservation minister, axed his permit, giving as a reason that he had killed the shark for commercial gain.

Hislop fought just as hard as the great white he'd taken. He lobbied the minister with his own collection of statistics of death and disappearances around the Victorian coast. His figures showed that 119 people had vanished along a 20-kilometre stretch of coastline since 1970. The 20 kilometres included Cheviot Beach, from where Prime Minister Harold Holt vanished in 1967.

The 'Shark Hunter as Conservationist' Theory

Hislop claimed he respects sharks and denied allegations that his shark-hunting career had neither scientific merit nor contributed to the conservation cause. He displayed letters of appreciation from scientific and educational institutions in other countries and within Australia to support his claims. They included an official letter from the Whale Foundation applauding his efforts to save the life of a minke whale stranded on a reef near Townsville in 1982.

Hislop even said his mission to catch and destroy dangerous sharks helped the conservation movement. 'I'm a true conservationist but the only tag that sticks is, "Hislop – Shark Killer," he complained. 'There are more than 300 species of sharks in the ocean and most of them are harmless and should be protected. I concentrate on the man-eaters – tigers and great whites. Each time I catch a great white and cut open its stomach, I find either a dugong or a penguin or a seal, even a young humpback whale is part of the white's diet. These are the very creatures greenies are worried about and I have saved thousands of them by catching the big sharks. Great whites are not endangered and never will be – not even if 10,000 Vic Hislops are out there catching them. They have no natural predators and their numbers are on the increase.'

The 'Serial Killer' Theory

In the 1980s and '90s Vic Hislop had many other run-ins with officialdom. Apart from the Phillip Island debacle, which had a touch of politics and theatre about it, his most memorable clashes have been in South Australia. In September, 1991, a 19-year-old Adelaide University student, Jonathan Lee, was killed by a white pointer off

Aldinga Beach, south of Adelaide (see page 83). Vic Hislop packed up his gear at his home in Cairns and headed south.

When he arrived in Adelaide he called a news conference, because by now he was deeply immersed in his battle with authorities and the conservation movement, and knew they would be using the media to promote arguments against him. He said that the 'pro-shark lobby had brainwashed the public'. At that conference he came up with a terrifying prospect while warning of what he saw as the dangers of letting killer sharks swim free. The great white which took Jonathan Lee, he suggested, could be a serial man-eater.

He stunned his audience when he said he strongly believed the shark that took Lee could be the same one that killed diver Terry Gibson at Marino Rocks off the southern suburbs of Adelaide on 18 September 1987, almost four years to the day earlier (see page 155). But he had even more guns to fire. He said he believed that fatal shark attacks in South Australia since the death in 1985 of Shirley Durdin near Port Lincoln (see page 155) could be the work of the same great white shark, returning each year to its territorial waters. He claimed the only way to stop its annual attacks was to let him try to catch it as soon as it struck again.

'We certainly should be trying to thin them out around the beaches,' he said. He said he was being thwarted by the South Australia Fisheries department which was fed research by pro-shark disciples who lacked his knowledge of shark habits. He went on to warn that more attacks were 'just a question of time' as the great whites returned to South Australia after spending winter along the Queensland coastline.

Already controversial, the shark-hunter told his audience that the attack on Lee was 'very predictable and won't be the last'. And he said a search of missing people records in South Australia during the past two years would reveal further shark deaths.

'There are at least six people unaccounted for during that time, including two sisters who disappeared while swimming near Port Lincoln,' he said. 'The interesting thing is that people disappear during the September–December period, the exact time frame when the great whites return to feed on baby seals.'

Also sitting in at the news conference was Ken Jury, a well-known and respected South Australian fisherman, media personality and then spokesman for the state's Fisheries department. In an ambush worthy of the great white, Jury questioned the shark hunter's qualifications and called on him to back up his claims with scientific evidence instead of personal 'anecdotes'.

Perhaps a little unnerved by the course of events at the news conference, Hislop agreed to a meeting the following day with the director of the Fisheries department, Rob Lewis. Lewis had accused Hislop of spreading fear and irrational thoughts. Hislop later described the meeting as a set-up and a waste of time, but took the chance to throw a few more broadsides into the argument.

He called on South Australian authorities to allow him the opportunity to hunt Jonathan Lee's killer before it struck again. He demanded an answer to his claim that human lives were being sacrificed in order to protect the great white 'killing machines', then let go with what he hoped would be a knockout punch.

'Rob Lewis told me we can afford to lose a few skin-divers but the great white shark is protected and that's it,' Hislop alleged.

Mr Lewis was not fazed. 'A lot of what Mr Hislop has been saying is not supported by a large sector of the community,' he said. 'I am aware of the certainty he has that he alone can capture the single shark responsible.' Mr Lewis said the department was involved in scientific research to find out more about the great white shark, but because it was not a commercial fish the funds available were limited. Mr Lewis won the match with a gracious invitation to Vic Hislop to make an appointment to see him so they could again discuss his theories.

The Shirley Durdin Attack

Hislop's mention at the news conference of Shirley Durdin referred to a horrific attack in March, 1985, at Port Lincoln. The 33-year-old mother of four was bitten in half while snorkelling as her husband and four young girls watched horrified from the shore. Her family saw the shark strike, but all that was ever found afterwards was a single orange flipper.

The Terry Gibson Attack

The reference to Terry Gibson concerned the disappearance of the 47-year-old professional diver off Marino Rocks, near Adelaide, in September1987. It was yet another incident when Hislop would confront his opponents head-on. But while tact has never been a big Hislop characteristic, he really did go overboard with some of his statements.

'The greenies and the filmmakers tried to make out that Terry Gibson's disappearance was an insurance fraud and nothing to do with sharks but his weight-belt was found with great white teeth marks all over it, and it was still buckled up,' he said. 'The last thing they wanted was Vic Hislop bringing in a big white with Terry Gibson in its guts. It would interfere with their plans to get the great whites protected.'

However tactless his statements may have been, he did have reason to be upset with the Fisheries inspectors. While he was at sea off Marino rocks hunting sharks, nine Fisheries officers in two boats cut his lines.

The Matthew Foale Attack
The following year, 1988, would provide yet another incident which Hislop would argue supported his serial shark theory.

Surfboard rider Matthew Foale was savagely attacked and killed 400 metres from the spot where Terry Gibson disappeared.

'It was probably the same shark that got Terry and quite possibly the same one that took Jonathon Lee,' Hislop was to say later.

The Port Lincoln "Serial Killer'
Then in 1989, Hislop was able to raise the spectre of another serial killer in the Port Lincoln area. He claimed a huge white pointer terrorizing people on small boats near Port Lincoln could be the monster that mauled Shirley Durdin

four years earlier. Mr Hislop said he was asked by locals to travel from his Queensland home to South Australia specifically to catch and destroy a particular shark. He told how the giant six-metre shark had circled, rolled out of the water and repeatedly rammed two small fishing boats off a small island inhabited by seals.

People in the boats were terrified at the *Jaws*-like encounter, fearing they would be capsized. Several vowed to stay off the water until the shark was caught. But he had no sooner set his lines than a Fisheries department boat arrived. Officers confiscated Mr Hislop's equipment which was deemed to be illegal. This was confirmed by the Fisheries department director, Rob Lewis.

Mr Lewis said he had received no advice about a shark problem at Port Lincoln. 'Mr Hislop is not a commercially licensed fisherman in South Australia and his equipment is not permitted for recreational fishing,' Mr Lewis said, sticking to the letter of the law. He added that Mr Hislop may be prosecuted.

Mr Hislop said he had been contacted by the owner of the property where the Shirley Durdin attack took place, and that the owner told him of a huge shark which was causing problems.

'A shark that has attacked a human returns to the same spot at the same time year after year,' Hislop said. He said sharks were coming closer to shore to hunt dolphins and seals because of dwindling tuna stocks in deeper waters.

The constant thread running through all of Vic Hislop's dire warnings is that people will continue to be taken by sharks. And the numbers of victims will rise with the growing number of sharks, because more will travel close inshore looking for food.

'People keep telling us that they are a beautiful creature and they've got to be protected, but a lot of human lives are going to be lost,' he said. 'All these sharks know is how to eat and devour. They are a killing machine and need to be thinned out.'

But neither science, nor politics, yet agrees with Mr Hislop. The white pointer shark is still very much an unknown quantity. A senior research officer with the South Australian Fisheries department, Barry Bruce, said there was no evidence to support an assumption that an individual white pointer would turn into a serial killer of humans.

He said there was little known about what influences sharks to attack and while great whites are commonly seen in near coastal waters, and seen to stay around in certain areas before moving on without positive means of identification of the individual sharks it is impossible to accurately determine their numbers.

So, despite being the largest predatory shark in the world, and the one that instills the most fear in the most people, according to science if not Vic Hislop, the white pointer is still the least known of all sharks.

The Case for Conserving Sharks

Kill and We Kill Ourselves

Technology is enabling us to destroy earth and its animals at a headlong speed that would have seemed unimaginable 50 years ago. Nothing is safe from greedy, short-sighted humanity. Rainforests burn so that farmers can plant cornflake-crops and fatten cattle for hamburgers. The oceans now are so ruthlessly over-fished that some staple species, which have fed humankind for millennia, are dwindling away.

The hardy species that remain are carrying in their flesh an increasing load of industrial and maritime pollutants – poisons that are causing increasing illness among the purportedly intelligent beings at the top of the food-chain: us.

Today it's apparent to most people that we must try to save the remaining environment and the living creatures we haven't yet decimated. But should we include man-eating sharks on our 'must-protect' list? The answer – in the view of ecologists and of relatively enlightened governments (like Australia's) – is *'yes'*.

Our oceans are a vast web of interdependent life. To destroy or seriously deplete elements of that life might be tantamount to toppling a row of dominoes while blindfolded.

It's doubtful that anyone on earth – even the possessor of the greatest mind – can guess what the effect of changing the oceans' ancient balance might be.

Sharks are at the summit of the sea's food-consuming hierarchy: linchpins of an infinitely complex symbiosis which has developed over hundreds of millions of years.

Man, in a fashion which has been likened to the effects of a fast-growing tumour in the body of the planet, is currently unbalancing that symbiosis – at a reckless pace.

Sharks, at a rate of millions per year, are dying at the hands of 'sporting' fishermen, drowning in the mesh of artificial beach barriers (see 'Should Sharknets Stay?' on page 168), perishing in the steel jaws of factory farms and dying in the sheer filth that burgeoning humanity creates.

As the human population grows, so does the run-off of raw effluent, pesticides and industrial waste into coastal waters. Some sharks choke on the mess and are washed ashore to rot. Others are driven from their natural fishing grounds by the algal blooms whose growth the pollution stimulates. Even escaping the algae doesn't deliver these fanged refugees from danger. Sharks are particularly vulnerable to heavy metals and organic chemicals, thought to inhibit their breeding ability.

This artificially induced reduction in the shark's reproduction rate is a major part of the ecological problem. Sharks are slow breeders, even under the most favourable conditions – but it's now becoming dramatically apparent that they are not replacing their numbers as rapidly as

ON 7 NOVEMBER 2000, the morning after Ken Crew was taken by a white pointer at Perth's North Cottesloe Beach, friends gathered to farewell him at an informal dawn ceremony. A popular member of The Pod, a year-round morning swimming group, Crew was the third person in Western Australia to be killed by a shark in 2000.

Photograph courtesy West Australian Newspapers

FORMER ST KILDA footballer Brian Sierakowski on the day of Crew's death. He had a brush with a shark at the same beach three years earlier. Miraculously he was almost unscathed. Sierakowski's AFL player son, David, is on the left.

Photograph courtesy West Australian Newspapers

THIS WHITER POINTER, feeding on a whale carcass, was photographed off Burns Beach, WA, less than two months before Crew's attack.

Photograph courtesy West Australian Newspapers

A HAPPY FAMILY OUTING turned to tragedy when Therese Cartwright was taken by a white pointer in 1993, while diving off Weymouth on Tasmania's north-east coast. Therese was the mother of six-year-old quads and an 11-month-old baby at the time.

Photograph courtesy the Mercury, *Hobart*

PROFESSIONAL DIVER Tony Szolomiak had a narrow shave in the same waters, only three months earlier. But this time the attacker was a three-metre tiger shark. Szolomiak managed to whack the shark on the snout with his spear gun, causing it to go into a convulsion. Meanwhile, Szolomiak made a hasty getaway.

Photograph courtesy the Mercury, *Hobart*

IN ONE OF THE MOST BIZARRE shark attacks ever, a white pointer dragged Michael Docherty off his surfboard with the leg rope still attached. For 20 minutes the creature dragged Michael's body up and down the bay, towing the surfboard behind. Here two close friends watch in helpless dismay. The attack took place in October 1992 at Queensland's Morton Island.

Photograph courtesy the Brisbane Courier Mail

'MIRACLE MAN' Rodney Fox was literally torn apart in a white pointer attack in St Vincent's Gulf in December 1961. After well over 400 stitches, his survival is considered a miracle. Today, he is regarded as *the* world shark expert. He is photographed with a life-size model of a white pointer.

Photograph courtesy Greg Adams and the Adelaide Advertiser

THESE ARE THE JAWS of the bronze whaler that attacked Leo Ryan as a young man at Burleigh Heads, Queensland, in 1950. Leo had a small tooth fragment removed from his lower spine in 1998 – almost 50 years after the attack.

Photograph courtesy Anthony Weate and the Brisbane Courier Mail

A HUGE TIGER SHARK disgorged a human arm at Coogee Aquarium in 1935 – before a horrified crowd. A tattoo on the arm eventually led police to identify it as being that of small-time criminal James Smith. This famous case is known as the Shark Arm Murder.

Photograph courtesy The Herald and Weekly Times Photographic Collection

LUCKY SURVIVOR, Henri Bource was attacked by a gigantic white pointer while swimming near Port Fairy, Victoria, in 1964. With his leg severed at the knee, he could easily have bled to death. Like Rodney Fox, he later became involved in a business involving cage dives among sharks.

Photograph courtesy Ian Baker and The Herald and Weekly Times Photographic Collection

THE GREAT WHITE SHARK, Greg Norman, with another great white, which he caught off Langton Island, 30 kilometres north-west of Port Lincoln, South Australia, in 1990. The unnecessary killing of this 488-kilogram beast caused a huge furore about the morality of killing sharks purely as trophies.

Photograph courtesy Neon Martin and the Adelaide Advertiser mankind is depleting them.

Scientists today are warning their governments that oceans containing 'insufficient' numbers of sharks might actually be *dangerous* to humanity. The bounty the oceans have always offered us – in terms of food, medicinal ingredients and much more – might no longer be available if we continue to tamper with the status quo.

Increasingly, governments in the richer countries are listening – and introducing 'species survival programmes' in an attempt to protect sharks and other threatened sea creatures.

The widespread 'kill the bastards' attitude toward sharks is primitive but compellingly understandable. It isn't easy, after someone has been attacked in the water, to take no action against the 'culprit'.

But Nature's inexorable logic is now forcing us to take a broader view. If we manage to rid earth's oceans of, say, the great white (a goal we might well achieve before this century ends) the effect will be incalculable. One theory – increasingly popular among scientists – is that driving the great whites to extinction will topple the dominoes below:

- With great whites no longer on the scene, their favoured prey species, such as seals, sea lions and dolphins, will increase in number.
- Because there are more of them, these former prey animals will eat greater numbers of fish and squid.
- It will become harder for us to find fish to harvest from the sea.
- As a direct outcome of destroying the great white,

humanity will have less food on its plate.

The early conservationists argued that we should preserve wildlife for humane and moral reasons.

Those principles still apply. But as our knowledge of the natural world increases, we're becoming aware of a new imperative:

We must refrain from destroying entire species, if we, ourselves, hope to survive.

(Reproduced by permission of John Pinkney.)

Stymied – by a Stupid Shark Law

*T*here's at least one wildlife protection law that simply doesn't make sense. The legislation's restrictive absurdity became obvious in 2000 – after Mosman Park (Western Australia) man Ken Crew was attacked and tragically killed by a large shark. (See description of attack, page 38)

Soon afterwards, the captain of a Fisheries department boat spotted what he believed was the killer – and followed it for two hours up and down the coast off Cottesloe. *But under the provisions of the state's shark protection act he had no permission to capture or destroy it!*

That permission would have had to be signed off by the Fisheries minister, who was in a Cabinet meeting at the time. The incident created public outrage – and helped convince the Western Australian government that it should urgently shake up its shark (and people) protection policies.

High on the list of proposals were aerial patrols – even though some experts doubted their usefulness. Ian Cowie, chairman of the government's shark awareness committee, pointed out that a plane surveying the long, straight coastline from Mandurah to Hillarys could sweep past a shark attack without the spotters noticing.

'Sharks move stealthily, often camouflaged against the background,' he said. 'They rarely swim close to the surface with their fins visible. We must be careful that people don't get a false sense of security – that because a plane is up there they are somehow guaranteed safety.'

The government looked also at sharknets (considered 'environmentally negative' – see 'Should Sharknets Stay', page 168) and shark fencing which, it was decided, would not withstand storms. Among other questions the Western Australian government asked itself were:

- If a shark is spotted five kilometres out to sea on a hot summer day when the surf is good, should we sound the alarm? Or do we watch it or try to chase it away?
- If a shark attacks, should it be caught or killed?
- If a shark simply comes in too close, should we try to capture it?

But most importantly – in the wake of the Mosman Park swimmer's death – the Western Australian government introduced new emergency procedures for its Fisheries employees.

They'll no longer be forced to wait for ministerial approval before dealing with a suspected killer shark.

A sensible decision that other state governments (all hogtied by the same restrictive law) might emulate.

(Reproduced by permission of John Pinkney.)

When and Where Sharks Attack

*D*awn and dusk are the traditional times for fishers to hit beaches and rivers in search of a catch. Sharks seem to agree that these are the finest times for hunting. And by inference, they're the worst times for mere humans to take a swim.

Surfboards, canoes and kayaks figure strongly in near-misses with sharks – which indicates that they offer some slight degree of protection. Never forget, though, that there's always the chance of an opportunistic shark deciding to pounce at any time and on anyone, 'protected' or not.

Most shark attack survivors have fallen foul of smaller species. Some have actually survived horrific encounters with the great white.

16 Ways to Avoid a Shark Attack

- DON'T swim, dive or surf where sharks are known to congregate.
- DON'T swim with dogs or other pets.
- DON'T swim in dirty or murky water.

- DON'T swim near people who are fishing or spear-fishing.

- DON'T carry dead fish when swimming or diving.

- DON'T swim at night, early in the morning, or early in the evening. These are the times when sharks are hunting.

- DON'T wear contrasting colours or flashing objects, such as jewellery – which may look to a shark like sunlight flashing off a fish's scales.

- DON'T wear a black diving suit – it may make you look to a shark like a seal.

- AVOID swimming far offshore, near channels, at river mouths or in waters that drop off steeply to greater depths.

- LEAVE the water if schooling fish begin to behave erratically, or congregate in large numbers.

- WATCH for places to which sharks might be attracted – such as stretches of water into which seabirds are diving.

- LOOK carefully before jumping into the water from a boat or pier.

- IF you see a shark or hear a shouted warning, swim calmly and rhythmically back to boat or beach. Move as quickly as possible – but don't **rush!** Sudden movements attract sharks.

- NEVER molest a shark of any kind – no matter how small it might be.

- STAY in a group with other swimmers, whenever possible.
- KEEP the shark in sight – particularly if you're swimming underwater. Survivors of most attacks say they never saw the predator. Sharks are often reported as having shied away from someone who **looked directly at them.**

7 Ways to Help Someone Bitten by a Shark

- TREAT the patient immediately, on site.
- STOP the bleeding immediately by applying **direct pressure** above or on the wound. If bleeding can't be controlled by a **pressure bandage**, use a **tourniquet**.
- REASSURE the patient.
- PHONE or send for an ambulance and medical help.
- DON'T move the patient further than the beach if he/she is badly injured.
- COVER the patient lightly with clothing or a towel.
- GIVE NOTHING by mouth.

Should Sharknets Stay?

Kind to People – but Cruel to Creatures

Sharknets were introduced to Australian beaches in 1936. For nearly 70 years since that time, there have been no shark attack deaths in coastal areas where nets are installed. This fact seems argument enough for keeping existing sharknets, adding new ones wherever possible – and installing, to the greatest feasible extent, a ring of protection around Australia's coasts.

But many conservationists disagree. Nets, they argue, do far more harm than good – playing havoc with the balance of nature on which we all depend.

One of the principal organizations seeking an end to netting is the World Wildlife Fund (WWF). In July 2001, a humpback whale calf drowned after becoming entangled in a net off the Gold Coast, while its distressed 20-tonne mother watched helplessly. This incident prompted the WWF to call yet again for reform. Dr David Butcher, CEO of the organization's Australian branch, urged that the deadly shark exclusion devices at least be removed from whale migration routes.

'These nets are responsible for killing significant numbers of marine mammals every year,' he said. 'Realistically they're nothing more than a form of marine debris. And it seems hypocritical to ask commercial fisheries to address the fatal effects of discarded fishing gear on marine life when state governments are funding shark control programmes that kill many protected species.' (The toll includes not only whales, but dolphins, manta rays and turtles.)

Dr Butcher added, 'The shark control programmes are obviously *out of control* in their effect on marine life.'

Conservationists have long complained that the nets are not only catching *dangerous* sharks but protected and *harmless* shark species also. A major victim is the fish-eating grey nurse.

And we might even be making a mistake by killing the majestic but terrifying great white which is dying in nets in significant numbers. No-one really knows what effects will flow from removing such a high-level predator from the marine food-chain.

Should Sharknets be Removed?

Yes	30%
No	22%
Just in Some Places!	47%

Source: Behind the News Poll

The Machine Gun Solution (1935)

Australians in the 1930s were so worried by the prospect of perishing in a shark's jaws that governments offered prizes and staged brainstorming meetings in the hope that some inventive member of the public might produce a solution.

Perhaps the most bizarre suggestion was offered by a New South Wales man, who recommended that machinegun nests be set up on headlands, to slay sharks swimming too close to shore. He also urged authorities to sow coastal waters with high-explosive boobytraps that would be tripped when a shark brushed by. Solutions, from a swimmer's viewpoint, which might have proved deadlier than the problem.

But it was the notion of nets that fired the imagination of the New South Wales and Queensland governments.

As we know them today, these predator-blocking devices are used on open ocean beaches – and comprise a rectangular piece of mesh suspended between buoys. Holes in the mesh are usually 50 centimetres wide – small enough to allow smaller fish through, while entangling sharks (and other larger creatures). The average sharknet is about 200 metres long, descending to a depth of six metres. Sinkers at the base, partnered by torpedo floats at the top, keep it upright in the water.

Around the Australian coast there are variations on this design. In addition to nets Queensland's shark control programme uses hooks baited with fresh fish and suspended from buoys to catch visiting sharks.

On some Australian harbour beaches authorities have erected rigidly constructed shark enclosures – within which beachgoers can swim safely. At first glance these water-fortresses seem preferable to nets. But builders have learned not to install them on open ocean beaches, where the power of the waves can start ripping them apart from the first day.

One downside of these comfortingly safe harbour enclosures is their tendency to cause beach erosion.

Are Nets Out of Date?

Environmentalists commonly argue that sharknets belong to a less enlightened era – a time when primeval public fear prompted governments to over-react.

The anti-netters point out that ten Australians are struck by lightning every year, while (statistically) less than one dies from a shark attack.

And the environmentalists are particularly fond of reminding us that although the United States is the nation that exported Spielberg's *Jaws* – the ultimate shark nightmare – it has never erected nets. Thanks to that omission, American governments have spared themselves the discomfort of facing legal action if ever a net or enclosure goes wrong, with resultant injuries to swimmers.

It's that daunting possibility of being sued which places Australian governments in a 'Catch-22' position. As the poll result on page 176 indicates, large numbers of Australians are increasingly comfortable with the idea of scrapping nets for the environment's sake.

But for the authorities, it isn't so easy. If nets are removed from a particular beach – and one, ten or 20 years later, someone is killed there by a shark – the family might sue for negligence and collect a million or three. Insurers would probably advise that Australian shark controllers retain the status quo – and the nets along with it.

Recorded Catch in New South Wales and Queensland Shark-Meshing Programmes

New South Wales		
Total Sharks	1972–90	4,485
Dolphins and Porpoises	1950–93	94
Dugongs	1950–93	5
Rays	1950–93	2,074
Killer Whale	1950–93	1
Queensland		
Total Sharks	1962–88	30,630
Dolphins	1962–88	520
Dugongs	1962–88	576
Turtles	1962–88	3,656
Rays	1962–88	13,765

Source: Biological Conservation Journal

Nets Spell Doom for Dugongs

A study released in 2001 shows that sharknets, combined with pollution and over-hunting by Aborigines has almost wiped out the dugong (sea-cow) population in seas off Australia's north-east coast.

The report, issued by James Cook University, found dugong numbers had declined by 97 per cent since 1963.

The report said the large sea-grazing mammal was being caught in sharknets strung along 48 beaches. The author, Professor Helene Marsh, said,

'The probable causes ... almost certainly include habitat loss and overkill from traditional hunting and drowning in commercial gill nets as well as the sharknets.'

The dugong – a distant relative of the elephant – can grow to about 400 kilograms. It is the only herbivorous mammal that lives in marine environments and exists on seagrasses which, before industrialization, grew in shallow, non-polluted waters.

Professor Marsh's report concludes that it would, under ideal conditions, take about 80 years for dugong numbers to recover to 1960 levels. 'Comprehensive management strategies' will be needed to prevent the dugong from becoming extinct.

(Reproduced by permission of John Pinkney.)

Protection Pods

Sharknets could soon be as out-dated as high-buttoned boots – if a new brand of technology reaches the market place.

In the mid-1990s the first real steps were taken towards devising a workable system to ward off marauding sharks from people in the water. Work was going ahead towards perfecting a device which was not so much an active defence mechanism, such as a spear-gun or powerhead, but a passive device which would prevent wandering sharks from even approaching a person in the water.

The disadvantage with spear-guns and powerheads is that the user generally only gets one shot at an approaching shark, and that one attempt may create more problems than it solves. The powerhead is literally an underwater shotgun. It carries a shotgun shell and the theory is that an endangered diver pushes it against the shark's body and pulls the trigger. The resulting blast either kills the shark, drives it away, or enrages it.

In any case, the powerhead, like the spear-gun, damages the fish, releasing blood into the water, which may serve only to attract other sharks in the area to investigate the commotion. How much better then to prevent sharks even approaching?

Countless formulas have been tried to develop an effective chemical-based shark-repellent. Massive amounts of time, effort and money has been poured into this research in a bid to protect people, especially service personnel, from shark attacks. One type of chemical repellent mimicked the reaction between seawater and the decaying body of a shark. Some others may have even been effective, but the limiting factor was time. One person can only carry so much chemical repellent, and the wind and waves would soon conspire to disperse and dilute even the thickest cloud of the strongest repellent once it was released into the water.

Scientists have battled for years to find an effective way to repel sharks. The quest became more urgent during World War II, when the United States navy looked for a way to protect downed pilots or sailors forced to abandon ships in the Pacific Ocean. Scientists at the Marineland Biological Laboratory in Flagler County participated in the shark repellent research, which resulted in development of a 'shark chaser' – a life jacket filled with chemicals repulsive to sharks.

But the jacket, as well as other devices that followed, proved ineffective. Through the years, scientists realized trying to turn sharks away with chemicals is impossible because the ocean dilutes chemicals to concentrations that don't bother sharks. 'You'd end up having a barge with people shovelling chemicals in the water all the time to keep it at levels offensive to sharks,' said George Burgess, a director of the International Shark Attack File in Gainesville, Florida.

But lately, electronics appear to offer a solution, the

Protective Ocean Device (POD), which is a self-contained electronic transmitter which can be worn with a wetsuit, or embedded in a surfboard. It was initially developed by a South African company, but was too big and bulky to be wearer-friendly. An Australian firm, the Adelaide-based Sea Change Technology, jumped into the water and perfected the device. The original South African development was tested in Australia's great white playground around Port Lincoln, with good results.

In 1996, Sydney aquarium curator, Ian Gordon, took to the water with prominent research team Ron and Valerie Taylor. Mr Gordon went swimming with five white pointer sharks off Port Lincoln, and afterwards said the device had 'incredible potential' for preventing attacks. He said it would help remove the hysteria surrounding sharks. Mr Gordon said the POD enabled him to swim closer to sharks than was previously possible without a cage. 'You were so struck by the beauty of the animal that you almost forgot to turn the unit on,' he said.

Development had reached the stage where the South Africans were set to launch the POD on the world market at an international event in Singapore, but they miscalculated. Their POD was too bulky and heavy for easy use in the water. It was 30 centimetres long, 15 centimetres wide and about 15 centimetres deep – about the size of a box of tissues.

A version of the South African POD was carried by divers, attached to their air tanks, as they swum under competitors in some events in Sydney Harbour at the 2000 Olympic games, but it was never going to be a commercial mass market success. Sea Change Technology took up the challenge, and have now perfected a POD which weighs less than one kilogram and can comfortably be worn by a diver of surfer.

The POD creates an 'invisible force-field' around swimmers. At first glance, the light, wallet-sized device that attaches around a surfer's ankle may not seem very protective compared to a steel cage divers sometimes use to protect themselves from a shark. But the device produces a strong electro-magnetic field that overwhelms the shark's sixth sense, consisting of pores or receptors on the head and nose.

Sharks use these pores, known as 'ampullae of Lorenzini', to navigate and find prey (see also page 216). The pores are incredibly sensitive, able to pick up the tiny electrical discharges from the nervous systems of the prey they are hunting. If a fish is injured it will give off distress signals which the shark receives as it closes in for the kill. But the POD generates a field of electro-magnetic energy, which is broadcast for several metres in all directions around a diver, surfer or swimmer. When the shark gets too close to the strong electrical field their receptors are overloaded with the energy from the device. The closer they get, the more their senses are scrambled and, in theory, they decide it's not worth the discomfort and turn away to hunt out an easier target.

Other fish are not affected because they do not have the same sophisticated electrical sensors that sharks have developed since they first appeared about 400 million years ago.

One of the first markets to see the POD is Volusia County in Florida in the United States, now regarded as the shark-bite capital of the world, with 22 attacks in 2001, fortunately none fatal. Sea Change Technology doesn't expect every surfer to rush down to their local surf-shop and snap up a POD, however. At this stage, they are just too expensive for the mass market, retailing at around $1,000 per unit. But the company does expect them to sell well to professionals, who make their money from being in the water all the time.

Sea Change is also considering whether these repellers can be adapted for other applications, such as being placed on anti-shark fences around popular beaches to provide another layer of protection for swimmers. They may also one day be fitted to commercial operations such as oil rigs or fish farms.

The POD is simply the latest development in a search that has been going on for decades to find some positive way of keeping people out of the inside of sharks. Even the use of electrical devices has been looked at extensively, but without success. In fact, some early tests finished with the test diver being electrocuted and the shark unaffected!

Over the years, some other weird and wonderful theories have been tried, all with little success. At one stage there was a programme to test the shark's reaction to loudspeaker systems broadcasting the sounds made by killer whales, the shark's only real danger in the oceans, and another supposedly scientific experiment involved painting divers' wetsuits with the colour scheme of poisonous sea snakes. Neither worked. Some researchers have also been studying the Moses soul fish in Middle Eastern waters, because it had been noticed that sharks appeared to be repelled by it.

Great Shark Legends and Other Amazing Tales

Where it All Started

*J*aws, the book, by Peter Benchley, and *Jaws,* the movie, by Steven Spielberg, sparked a massive worldwide interest in sharks of all types, but especially in the man-eaters. Prior to the book and the movie, shark attacks were curiosities. They happened to fishermen, or people too stupid or slow to get out of the way. They were a talking point for a day or two in the immediate area, then went down as bad luck or bad timing.

But since the two *Jaws* came along to give everyone nightmares, sharks have been seen in a different light. Researchers have gone back over the local history books, dug around in old newspaper file rooms and scoured municipal records to bring together and collate hundreds and hundreds of little-known details about attacks, fatal and otherwise, which were previously regarded as local folklore and legend. Squads of scientists are now involved in shark research, trying to understand why these ancient life forms have evolved to where they are, and why their evolution seemed to stop tens of thousands of years ago, leaving them as living relics of by-gone eons.

This interest has sparked moves to protect sharks, especially the great white, in some countries, including Australia. There is a total ban on the taking of great whites in any Australian waters, which always leads to spirited debate in the newspaper letters pages whenever one of the majestic beasts kills or maims a person.

There are dozens of websites dealing with sharks. Some concentrate on the more bloodthirsty aspects of their lives, others concentrate on pictorial displays of sharks in their habitat, and still others provide a means of recording all aspects of the lives of sharks in the world's oceans, especially when their lives cross the boundary and begin inter-acting with human lives. This up-swelling of public interest can be traced back to Benchley and Spielberg. But even their heart-stopping work can be traced further back, to a series of shark attacks along the American east coast beaches south of New York.

Terror in American Waters, 1916

As it happened, *Jaws*, the fictional book and movie, bear a startling resemblance to what happened in real life. It was mid-summer in America, July 1916, and by any set of figures the country was in great shape. While Australia's young men were off fighting the war to end all wars in Europe and the Middle East, America was basking in a golden age of economic prosperity, not yet drawn into the war.

At the height of the 'season', New Yorkers by their thousand escaped the stifling heat and humidity which still makes the city almost unbearable through summer. They trooped en-masse to the seaside resorts in neighbouring New Jersey, and it can be fairly said that the events of that summer sparked the eventual creations of Benchley and Spielberg. *Jaws* told of mass panic among holiday-makers, attempted cover-ups so as not to do any economic harm, reward posters, scientists sensing fame and fortune and vigilante squads out for shark's blood.

The book and the film were eerily close to the reality that struck America's eastern seaboard that summer. The attacks were eventually compiled into some sort of order by Richard Fernicola in *Twelve Days of Terror* and also in *Shark Attacks* by Thomas Allen. Combining their efforts provides the following gripping account of a string of incidents which changed the focus of thinking about sharks and led to a best-selling book and one of the scariest movies ever made.

The Charles Vansant Attack

Bathing was a recreation which had become popular only in the previous two decades, and there were guidebooks to instruct the timid on how to cope with seawater. By 1 July 1916, the hotels were fully booked, even in a tranquil little resort such as Beach Haven, located on the narrow, 28-kilometre stretch of Long Beach Island in South Jersey.

New arrival Charles Vansant stood out among the crowds. The tall, good-looking, 25-year-old Honours graduate had a promising career as a broker before him. His father and sister Louise followed him down to the beach as Charles waded in. Beyond the waves, chest-deep in the water, he turned and started calling to the lifeguard's dog that had been playing with him in the surf but had suddenly swum back to shore.

Charles must have thought that people on the beach were joining in when they shouted, too, but they had seen a dark shadow behind him and a fin cutting through the water. Charles's shouts turned into screams. He was seen struggling back towards the beach, surrounded by a widening circle of blood. The lifeguard rushed to pull him away from the shark which, witnesses said, was still biting at the young man's thigh.

Two other men helped form a human chain and laid Vansant on the sand, his left leg virtually torn from his body. A tourniquet was applied but Charles fainted before he could be carried up the beach and placed on the manager's desk in a hotel. He died without regaining consciousness. Beach Haven residents then helped pay for steel netting to be placed 300 metres out to sea along the entire length of the beach.

Yet, strangely, the public reaction to this shark attack, the first recorded on the eastern seaboard of the United States, was low key. The event was considered bizarre. No-one believed that sharks attacked humans or even came close to shore.

Dr Frederick Lucas, director of the American Museum of Natural History, wrote that 'cases of shark-bite are usually found to have been due to someone approaching a shark impounded or tangled in a net, or gasping on the shore'. Dr John Nichols, Curator of Fishes at the same museum, and Dr Robert Murphy of the Brooklyn Museum, agreed sharks were scavengers which did not attack people.

In the late 1800s, Hermann Oelrichs, a prominent New York banker, had offered a $500 prize to anyone who could prove that a bather had actually been attacked by a shark anywhere north of Cape Hatteras in North Carolina. By 1916, the prize had gone unclaimed for 25 years.

The Charles Bruder Attack

In New Jersey, preparations for Independence Day continued. One of its most elegant and fashionable resorts was Spring Lake, 70 kilometres north of Beach Haven. Here, on 4 July 1916, the governor of New Jersey and assorted socialites watched the fireworks. They would all have come in contact with Henry Nolan, the lift driver, and Charles Bruder, the 28-year-old Swiss head porter.

On Thursday, 6 July, after changing at the employee bath-houses, the two men joined friends in the surf. The water was cold, and soon Bruder was alone, swimming 100 metres from the beach. Two shrill shrieks were followed by a bloodcurdling scream. The lifeguards saw what looked like a red canoe upturned in the water; in fact, it was Bruder in a pool of his own blood.

'A shark bit me! Bit my legs off!'' he cried. The guards hoisted him into the boat. Both his legs had been torn away just below the knees. Suffering a huge loss of blood, Bruder died before they reached the shore.

This time, the man-eater could not be ignored. Within 12 minutes of the attack, the water had been cleared of swimmers along 30 kilometres of the New Jersey coast. While local mayors installed 'shark-proof' wire netting and sent out armed motorboat patrols, the three wise university men, doctors Lucas, Nichols and Murphy, led an investigation.

Even now they were cautious, opining that further attacks were extremely unlikely. But, suddenly, sharks were everywhere and shark-hunters were out in force. Newspapers did their best to reassure holiday-makers, who were now pouring in by the thousands. President Woodrow Wilson, who would shortly be one of them, knew he might suffer in the forthcoming presidential election if he did not show concern.

The Matawan Attacks

But then came the events at Matawan, a quiet little town of 1,200 people, 25 kilometres from the ocean, connected by a tidal creek to Raritan Bay. It had no fashionable hotels, nor even a municipal pool – just a swimming hole in the creek near a disused wharf. Everyone knew everyone else. Police Chief Mulsoff doubled as the town barber; 24-year-old Stanley Fisher, a blond giant of a man, was tailor and dry-cleaner. William Stillwell worked at the sawmill; his young son Lester, who had epilepsy, was apprenticed there.

On the afternoon of Wednesday, 12 July, Charles Van Brunt arrived at the basket factory where his friends Lester and Ally O'Hara were doing summer work. The temperature was about 35°C, and at 3pm the three boys left for Matawan Creek. Earlier that day, 12-year-old Joseph Dunn and his elder brother Michael had set off from New York City by train to visit their aunt who lived in Cliffwood Beach on the north side of the creek.

At 2.30pm, an old sea captain, Thomas Cottrell, returning from a fishing trip in Raritan Bay, was crossing a drawbridge when he saw a formidable dark grey shape, about 2.5 metres long, making its way up the creek on the incoming tide. Astounded, he phoned police. Cottrell set out in a motorboat to warn creek swimmers of the shark's presence, then ran up Main Street to warn the boys. He missed them by minutes. Seconds after the captain had gone past, Lester, Ally and Charles, along with three more friends, arrived at the wharf, stripped and dived into the water. Ally O'Hara felt a sandpaper-like object graze his leg, looked down and saw what seemed to be the tail of a sea monster. While Lester Stillwell was over the deepest bit, he screamed.

The boys scattered and ran naked up Main Street shouting: 'Shark! A shark's got Lester!' Stanley Fisher dashed out of the dry-cleaners. The town carpenter, Arthur Smith, and another man, Red Burlew, joined him. The swimming hole water was red. The men hung chicken wire across the banks to keep the boy's body from being carried away. They prodded with poles, then began making dives through the murk to find Lester. Fisher dived to the bottom and thought he saw a body. Smith's stomach was painfully scraped by something moving.

Fisher was out of the water now but, seeing Lester's parents standing agonized on the bank, he went back for one last dive. Grabbing what remained of the boy, Fisher brought him to the surface, but in waist-deep water, was slammed by the shark and tottered backwards. Men in a boat helped Fisher get to the creek, with bone exposed and blood spurting. A makeshift stretcher was organized to take Fisher to the train station and on to hospital.

About 800 metres upstream, the Dunn boys, who had

arrived from New York City, and three others were swimming near a dock. Hearing the faint cries of 'Shark!', they raced to the dock ladder and hauled themselves up.

Joseph Dunn, the youngest and farthest away, had his hands on the bottom rung when he was tugged away and across the creek. The other boys created a human chain; Michael grabbed his brother's hand to tug him free. Just then, Cottrell appeared in the motorboat. He bundled up the boy and took him to the Matawan wharf where Joseph was taken by car to the hospital. 'It was like a big pair of scissors pulling at my leg,' he told people after he recovered.

It was two hours before Stanley Fisher reached hospital. 'I did my duty,' were his last words, mouthed in a whisper, before he died 90 minutes later.

Meanwhile, the angry citizens of Matawan patrolled the creek with shotguns and dynamite. On 14 July, the same day that Lester Stillwell's mangled body was discovered in Matawan Creek, a New York taxidermist named Michael Schleisser and his friend John Murphy went out in a three-metre motorboat into Raritan Bay. They had dropped a dragnet a few kilometres from the mouth of Matawan Creek to catch some pan fish for breakfast. A violent tug in the net stalled their motor. Schleisser hit a thrashing shark with an oar handle until it stopped moving.

The two men towed the 160-kilogram white shark – just a baby – back to the dock where it was dissected. Its stomach held human flesh and seven kilograms of bones. It was almost certainly the man-eater. There were no more attacks recorded in 1916, and no confirmed shark deaths off America's coastline for another 20 years.

The Shark Arm Murder

Mouldering in some dusty government warehouse are the records of one of the most bizarre shark tales the world has heard. It all began about a week before Anzac Day (25 April) in 1935, and as yet has not been successfully concluded. After this length of time it has to be more likely than not that the tale will never be wrapped up satisfactorily.

Back between the wars commercial shark fishing was a thriving industry in the waters of Sydney Harbour. One of the fishermen, a man called Bert Hobson, set several fixed lines a few kilometres out in the harbour off Coogee, which was home port to quite a fleet of professional fishing boats. The following day he returned to check his lines, and found a huge tiger shark thrashing around, desperately trying to get free. The beast was hopelessly tangled, and it gave Hobson an idea. He and his brother ran the aquarium back on shore at Coogee, and since the shark was still alive he thought it would be a good idea to tow it back and release it in the enclosure. They could bill it as the world's only tiger shark in captivity, and make a pretty penny charging sightseers for a look.

By now the shark was exhausted so it was relatively easy to tow it towards shore and get it into the enclosure.

However the great beast was suffering, moving slowly through the water, obviously ill and listless. Unwilling to let such a golden opportunity go easily, the Hobsons pumped oxygen through the water, and the shark seemed to pick up.

The Anzac Day holiday arrived and by 4.30pm, after the march, the reunions and two-up games in the pubs around Sydney, the Coogee Aquarium was doing a roaring trade. The captured tiger shark suddenly put on a spurt of activity, making two or three rushes from one end of the aquarium to the other, then it stopped and without warning regurgitated the contents of its stomach. The sightseers were morbidly fascinated, but the fascination turned to horror when a complete human arm emerged from the murk vomited up by the shark, and floated to the surface of the water. What's more, a length of rope was clearly visible, tied around the wrist of the arm.

To add to the fascination the story generated, it quickly became clear the captured tiger shark was not the animal which originally swallowed the arm. A much smaller shark had first become hooked on Bert Hobson's fixed bait-line. Its frantic struggles sent a signal to the much larger cruising tiger, which closed in for an easy feed. But in its frenzy the larger fish became trapped as well, only to be dragged off to the aquarium the following morning. It was found later that the arm had been lodged in the stomach of the smaller shark.

The arm was gingerly removed from the water, and police stepped in to take up the hunt. The most obvious clue as to whom the arm had originally belonged was a tattoo on the bicep: a rough depiction of two boxers, sparring. The arm was also preserved well enough to allow fingerprints to be taken from the hand, which made identification quick and positive. The fingerprints and tattoo were studied in great detail by police and forensic specialists at the Sydney morgue, who also called in Doctor Victor Coppleson, the leading expert at the time on shark wounds. Doctor Coppleson ascertained the arm had not been bitten from the rest of the body by a shark. His examination of the remains indicated it has been cut from the rest of the body by someone using a knife, rather than torn-off by the teeth of a shark. With that news, police realized they had been handed a unique murder investigation, and one in which all of Sydney, not to mention Australia and the world, was taking a keen interest.

With the fingerprints and the tattoo it did not take long to establish that the arm was that of James Smith, a 40-year-old small time criminal with a number of convictions. Smith had not been seen since 7 April of that year, when he left his Gladesville home after telling his wife he was going fishing. Smith had at various stages worked as an S.P. bookmaker, had operated a billiards parlour and gone bankrupt in the building trade. When the police began looking into Smith's recent movements, they discovered he had been sharing a house in what was then a small seaside village called Cronulla with a man called Patrick Brady. He was another small time villain, regarded as an extremely competent forger and well-known to the investigators. His criminal record went back over 20 years.

But the discovery of the shared accommodation by the two men came about through a stroke of good luck for the detectives. A barman at Cronulla's Cecil Hotel told police he had seen Brady drinking there with another man who answered the description of the still-missing Smith. Further checks revealed Brady had rented a beach-house for what now seems the ridiculously small amount of $3 per week. It was a holiday cottage, right on the beach, with its own boatshed. The estate agent described Brady as an excellent tenant, who left the house spotless when he moved on.

However, on further questioning, the agent came up with some puzzling aspects of Mr Brady's tenancy. He told detectives a mattress had been replaced, an old tin storage chest was missing but had been replaced with a smaller one, and an anchor was missing from the boatshed. A pair of weights from the cottage's sash windows was also missing.

The police then poured more efforts into tracing the movements of Brady in the period leading up to the unsightly shark vomit back at the Coogee Aquarium. Just as the barman at the Cecil came forward with a break the police needed in tracing Smith's movements, a Cronulla taxi driver also came forward to help them out with Brady. The cabbie recalled taking Brady to the well-to-do north shore, and dropping him off at a house which turned out to be that of popular boat-builder, Reginald Holmes. The North Shore gentleman was regarded as a pillar of his local church, and had made a very large fortune from his boat-building business. The apparent links between criminals

Smith and Brady, and a wealthy boat-builder from the North Shore, roused the curiosity of police. They went on to discover that Smith had been involved with the boat-builder in the purchase of an expensive yacht, the *Pathfinder,* which had mysteriously sunk.

A claim was made on the insurance company for the value of the lost boat, but the claim was suddenly withdrawn for no apparent reason. With all this information at their fingertips, police decided what was left of James Smith had to be in the tin trunk which was missing from the Cronulla beach-house. However, a thorough line search of the Cronulla sand dunes turned up nothing, as did countless sweeps by boat of the water in the Port Hacking area. At one stage police even hired a plane for an aerial search over the water and the shoreline.

Three weeks after the shark disgorged its grisly meal at the aquarium, police hauled Brady in for a tough questioning session. He told them nothing except what they already knew, but he did admit knowing Reginald Holmes. For his part Holmes was unshakeable in his denials that he knew Brady, even when the two men were presented to each other face to face. In a bid to break the stories of one or both men, Brady was arrested and charged with the murder of Smith.

The police evidence was flimsy to say the least. They had circumstantial evidence and traces of blood found in a kerosene tin. At this point Mrs Brady stepped in. She had convinced herself her husband was covering-up for Reginald Holmes and made a statement to that effect to police. Brady then made a fresh statement, maintaining his innocence in the matter of Smith's disappearance and presumed murder, but dropping Holmes in very deep water. He said he had last seen Smith on 9 April, two days after the murdered man had told his wife he was going fishing. Brady told detectives Smith left the seaside cottage with Holmes and another man. He also revealed he and Holmes were plotting a major crime involving a forged cheque.

Armed with the revised version of Brady's story, police made plans to bring Holmes in for another grilling. Whether he got wind of the detective's intentions, or whether the sheer pressure got too much for him we will never know, but Holmes decided it was time to make himself permanently unavailable. Fortified by most of a bottle of brandy, the boat-builder launched a newly completed speedboat from his yard at dawn on 20 May. Once out in the harbour, near where the Opera House now stands, he pulled a pistol from his pocket and held it to his head. He may have had a change of heart at the last split second, or the gentle rocking of the boat may have thrown his aim off, but the bullet he fired did not put an end to all his troubles. The impact knocked him into the water, but seconds later he surfaced and clambered back aboard his speedboat, blood gushing from a serious, but far from fatal, head wound.

The Sydney Water Police then began receiving frantic phone calls from members of the public and other officers, telling of a man covered in blood driving a boat at high speed all around the harbour. Two police launches were sent to investigate, and the chase that followed was like something from a Bond movie. Holmes led police on a merry chase, weaving between other moored boats, missing buoys and channel-markers by a hair's breadth and whipping in and out of the large and small bays that make up the Sydney Harbour coastline. The chase lasted about two hours before Holmes gave up and shut down the speedboat engine. Still covered in blood he called out to the police for bandages, and claimed he did not know it was police who were chasing him. Who he thought it was he didn't say.

On 24 May, four days after the mad chase, Holmes was allowed out of hospital, where he had been under constant police guard. During his recovery he made several statements to detectives which thoroughly implicated Brady in the murder of Smith. He claimed Brady admitted the murder to him, and said he'd dumped the body outside Port Hacking in the tin trunk which was missing from the beachhouse. Holmes also claimed Brady had threatened to kill him or have him killed if he spoke to police. He was allowed to go home after pledging to repeat his statements in the witness box as the star witness for the prosecution when an inquest into the death of Smith was held.

The inquest date was set for 12 June, almost a fortnight away. But amazingly police did not provide Holmes with any security or protection. Early on the morning of the day set down for the inquest a police patrol car came across another vehicle parked in The Rocks area, under the then three-year-old Sydney Harbour Bridge. The man inside was slumped over the wheel in the classic pose of a driver who has had too much to drink, and decided to sleep it off. The car's headlights were on and a door was open when the police pulled up alongside. Reginald Holmes had been shot twice, and unlike his own suicide attempt, whoever did the job had not missed. He was as dead as James Smith. Patrick Brady was in the clear on this murder. He was in police custody when Holmes was killed. However, police remembered the claims Holmes had made of Brady threatening to have him killed, and eventually arrested and charged two men with his murder.

But after two trials, and despite the prosecution having two eye witnesses, both men were acquitted. In time and because of a lack of evidence, Patrick Brady also walked free. But the shark arm murder did not go away for many years, at least not until all the main players in the whole saga had died. Whisper and rumour, threatening letters and anonymous phone calls to police, continued about the case. And, officially at least, the file is still open as a murder investigation. As for the huge tiger shark which made a meal of a smaller shark, which had already made a meal of James Smith's arm, it was destroyed the day after coughing up the one piece of evidence that sparked the whole gripping tale.

Sheer Shark Madness!

*T*hroughout human history men and women have accepted challenges that risked life and limb. The first caveman, for instance, who went up against a sabre-toothed tiger with nothing more than a sharpened stick; the early explorers, who sailed over the edge of the known world seeking riches and land for their monarchs. Hillary on Everest, Yuri Gagarin (the first man in Space), and Neil Armstrong (the first man on the Moon). They all succeeded at projects which had cost the lives of many who tried before them. Their deeds were carefully thought out, all the known dangers minimized as far as possible, and while there were plenty of unknowns, all the knowns had been considered and taken into account to make success and safety as sure as possible.

On the other hand, there are the others who are simply foolhardy, and for whom the Darwin Awards are handed out each year. The Darwin Awards are given, posthumously, to people who collectively raise the standard of the human gene pool by losing their lives in stunningly stupid stunts. And it would seem Australia has its fair share of candidates for a Darwin. For some reason, a rash of shark-patting broke out in mid-2001. Commercial ferry boats even went well off their normal route so hundreds of passengers could watch the spectacle.

The Pointer-patting Incident

It all started on a mid-winter Sunday in July when the carcass of a 15-metre southern right whale was seen floating in the chilly waters of Cape Jervis. Whale experts and fishermen were still debating whether the large mammal had died of natural causes, or had been hit by the Sealink vehicular ferry which plied a regular route between Cape Jervis on the southern tip of the Fleurieu Peninsula and Kangaroo Island, through waters known as the Backstairs Passage.

The fishermen preferred to believe it had been run down by a ship, possibly even the Sealink ferry, because there were paint marks on its skin. Various experts, however, were opting for natural causes. Deb Kelly, a manager with the National Parks and Wildlife Service, said there was no evidence to indicate the whale died from anything other than natural causes. She said that at 15 metres in length it was a fully grown specimen.

As they argued, the sightseers gathered. Among them were Chris Royans and his 24-year-old son, Luke. As their boat bobbed alongside the floating carcass, two kilometres offshore from Cape Jervis, five white pointers made a meal of the whale, tearing off great chunks of blubber and flesh.

One of the smaller sharks, a three-metre white pointer, let go of the dead whale's tail and disappeared below the water, but seconds later gently broke the surface, lazily looking at the people in the boat with its unfathomable eyes. From less than a metre away, Chris Royans reached out and grabbed its snout. Luke Royans followed his father's lead seconds later, in front of hundreds of witnesses. Hundreds of tourists witnessed the shark-patting from their vantage points aboard the Sealink ferry, which had moved five kilometres off-course to get to the area.

Incredibly, the Royans were distant relatives of Jevan Wright, the 17-year-old surfer taken by a great white near Elliston, a few hundred kilometres west, less than a year earlier (see page 35). Even more unbelievable, Luke Royans was an abalone diver, and great whites are close to the top of the list of things to be avoided in the world of the 'ab diver'.

Afterwards he said that close-up the great whites don't look like the aggressive man-eaters they are reputed to be, but he also acknowledged they deserve respect. It's difficult to tell where the respect should start, but an abalone diver grabbing one on the snout while leaning out of a boat does not seem to be giving the shark due respect.

Somebody reasonably qualified to comment, Kay Fox, labelled the exercise 'idiotic machismo'. She's the wife of shark attack survivor and now documentary maker, Rodney Fox. 'They can move so fast their whole body can come out of the water,' she said. 'Sharks don't swim around frantically but they can move fast if they have to. They can rocket up at a million kilometres an hour and bite your head off.'

Stating the obvious, she said it was not a good idea to

try patting them, and the Royans may have been lucky because the shark's normal behaviour had been modified by the abundance of free food on the carcass of the whale. Food they did not have to exert themselves for.

But there was more to come within a week. News that a 15-metre floating smorgasbord for great whites could be seen from Cape Jervis enticed thousands of people to head south from Adelaide. The trip was only a few-score kilometres, and took in the wine-growing areas of McLaren Vale ... all in all a very pleasant way to spend a lazy weekend. Just to add to the attraction, there was always the chance of seeing yourself on television, because the Adelaide channels had all scrambled crews to the southern tip of the Fleurieu Peninsula. And they were not to be disappointed.

A Whale of a Walk

Paul Williamson, a 34-year-old fisherman who used to work with Sealink (whose ferry may have started the whole bizarre escapade by ramming the southern right whale in the first place), found himself an instant celebrity. For a week he had been helping attempts to get the whale carcass, and the great whites it had attracted, further offshore.

Then, in one of those moments which can prove to be enduringly fascinating or suddenly fatal, he moved to the edge of the boat he was aboard. A second later he stepped off the boat, and onto the floating carcass, as the school of great whites continued to feed from beneath him. Paul Williamson was walking on the main course, with no apparent thought that he could become part of the meal.

Although he later apologized for the act of bravado, it was a half-hearted apology. In any case he became a local hero, suddenly achieving legend status which he was unwilling to totally give up. He even tried to convince his detractors that it was a perfectly safe act, which anyone could have done. As pictures of him astride the dead whale, giving a victory salute, flashed around the globe he attempted to justify the deed. 'The thing is huge, it's over 30 tonnes and more solid than any boat out there,' he said of the southern right carcass. It's a bit of a crazy thing to do, but it's not as dangerous as people have made it out to be. It was a matter of nosing right up to it and feeling the surface. It's not like I jumped on it or anything.'

Mr Williamson wandered around and took some photos before hopping back, fortunately in one piece, onto his own boat. In the days that followed he was forced to defend himself again and again, which he did, unwilling to throw off his 15 minutes of fame as an instant celebrity. South Australia's Environment minister of the time, Iain Evans, slammed Mr Williamson, saying he was appalled at such stupid behaviour. But his voice went largely unheard and as events a month later showed, unheeded.

In the meantime Paul Williamson and other business people at Cape Jervis were making the most of the mid-winter tourist rush. The local tavern rushed a series of T-shirts, caps and stubbie holders into production, some bearing the slogan, 'He walked on the whale and lived to tell the tale'. Another slogan, 'Don't be nervous, pat a white pointer at Cape Jervis,' was even more blatant, and potentially more dangerous.

Mr Williamson brushed off wave after wave of criticism, and also tried to deflect his detractors by harking back to the incident a week earlier when Chris and Luke Royans grabbed the snout of a white pointer feeding at the same shark restaurant where he went walking on the tables.

'It's just a stunt I did, it was safe and there were locals about,' he said during one interview, although what good the locals would have been – except as witnesses at an inquest – if the carcass had rolled escaped all but himself. 'There was definitely a bit of risk involved, but it was minimal. The water was dead flat. There's a bit of silliness in it, but there are a lot more dangerous stunts out there, like car racing.'

The clincher came when Mr Williamson was describing how he spent the week before his whale-walking stunt, while he was supposed to be helping tow the dead beast out to sea. 'The whole week has been fantastic. We saw heaps of sharks, one was about 18 or 20 feet (six or seven metres) long. The only time I got scared was when I saw fins on either side of my boat,' he said. 'You get a lot closer to the sharks on the boat … I would never pat them though. The only thing I was disappointed with was the television cameras being there. I wouldn't have done it then if I had known.'

Tourists Fuel a Feeding Frenzy

A month later, near the end of August, the authorities again had reason to express extreme disquiet. It seemed the whole of South Australia, especially anyone within striking distance of the coast, had gone shark-raving mad. Again a dead whale was at the centre of proceedings, but this time it involved the left-overs from a whale which had been dissected for scientific purposes after being washed up on a beach. After the dissection, word quickly spread through the area that sharks were about (not that they were rare since the coastline is dotted with seal colonies), and a large pack had gathered at Sceale Bay.

Some groups of people launched boats into the bay after loading up with whale blubber, while many others, including children, watched from the clifftop. The ones on the cliff were also armed with chunks of blubber and whale meat. Unlike those feeding on the Cape Jervis whale carcass, the Sceale Bay sharks went into a feeding frenzy. Several times the small boats carrying so-called tourists were bumped by sharks up to five metres long.

When the authorities arrived they were horrified to find the crowd on the clifftop throwing whale blubber into the mass of sharks below, and even more horrified to see people in small boats feeding the sharks, and encouraging their children to 'pat' the white pointers. Police and fisheries inspectors with officers from the Parks and Wildlife Service warned the people on the cliff, and those in the boats, to stop baiting the sharks, lest they themselves become shark bait.

Dr Deb Kelly, the manager with Parks and Wildlife who was sought out for comment on one of the incidents a month earlier, was even more angry at the Sceale Bay event.

'There is a very real case here for charging someone

with reckless endangerment of life ... particularly where children are close to feeding sharks, supposedly supervised by parents,' she said. Nobody was charged; perhaps officialdom pointing out the stupidity of getting anywhere near a shark pack in feeding mode was enough to bring the crowd to its senses. But Dr Kelly again repeated her warning that sharks are quite capable of leaping out of the water to seize prey. She could not explain, however, except as a freak circumstance, why the waters of South Australia that year seemed to be literally shark infested.

Afterwards, a Sceale Bay businessman, Grant Hobson, said local residents were not part of the shark-baiting spectacle which could so easily have turned into a multiple tragedy. 'A fatal shark attack, particularly on a child, is not something for which we want a reputation,' he said with masterful understatement.

A Blue Buddy

How many people would treat a shark the same way they'd treat the family dog? Feeding it, patting it, giving it a scratch and a hug. Not too many, hopefully, but South Australian fisherman, Dean Woodward, is the exception to the rule. The professional cray-fisherman and his mate spent a pleasant hour playing with a blue shark a few kilometres out to sea off Robe in February 1993. At one stage he even held the three-metre blue in a bear hug. Mr Woodward and his fishing mate, Tony Dawson, also from Robe, continually fed the shark, patted it on the head and body and even rubbed its eyes. They said it never even looked like attacking, and took pictures to prove it.

'We could have played with it all day,' Mr Woodward said. 'I have never experienced anything like this and probably never will again.'

The two men said the shark just seemed to be in a playful mood when they came across it while checking their craypots. 'Tony started feeding him and I went over to see what it was all about,' Mr Woodward said. 'We just drifted there playing with it for an hour. I wouldn't feed it with my hand but used a piece of wire poked through a bait. Once he missed the fish head and went under the boat, turned deep and came straight back up at me.'

That was when the blue came out of the water, and Mr Woodward decided on an even greater show of affection. 'I grabbed him in a bear hug, he didn't mind at all,' he said. 'I had no fear at all of him, even though he could have got me any time.' Mr Woodward said at one stage he held most of the shark out of the water by its dorsal fin and it pulled away from him and struck him lightly on the shoulder with its tail. 'Apart from that nothing happened, I couldn't believe it,' he said. 'I grabbed its tail and it gradually pulled away; it was amazing.'

Mr Woodward said he would 'keep an eye out' for the shark next time he was in the area, and would have no hesitation trying to feed it again.

While not encouraging anyone to treat a shark like a family pet, South Australia's resident shark expert, Rodney Fox, said Mr Woodward and his mate would have been relatively safe. He described blue sharks as fairly tame, and while they have been known to attack people they have small mouths, and therefore a small bite.

Greg Norman – and the Other Great White Shark

*O*ne of Australia's greatest money-spinning shark exports is not in the form of fillets or other by-products. It's a trademark, a brand name, a great marketing tool and enormously successful, known throughout the world as the 'Great White Shark': Golfer, Greg Norman.

And it's not all legend how he came to get the nickname which he has turned into a multi-million dollar business. It does have to do with some actual contact between Norman and a couple of great whites back in 1990.

The golfer was already a big name in the United States, and true to form American sports writers were trying to label him. They had Jack Nicklaus, the golfing legend of the day, tagged as the 'Golden Bear' and were hunting around for a catchy title to give to the interloper from down under who was blazing his way around the professional circuit. Initially they came up with the 'Polar Bear', largely because of his shock of white-blond hair and because he came from the continent down under, much closer to the South Pole than America is to the North Pole.

Ignoring the fact that Polar Bears make their home in the northern hemisphere, and it would be a cold day in Hell before one is seen in the Antarctic, the American sportswriters persevered. But the 'Polar Bear' tag never really stuck.

Then, thankfully for the sportswriters, myth and legend took over. Stories, tall tales really, began getting around the golf circuit, in the change rooms and bars, about this Aussie wonder who, when he wasn't blitzing them on the fairways, was brushing aside marauding sharks in Brisbane's Moreton Bay. And while privately laughing at the impossible tales, Australians continued to perpetuate the myth to the more gullible Americans. So the American sportswriting and reading fraternity gobbled all this up with glee, then someone came up with the 'Great White Shark' tag, and the rest, as they say, is history.

Almost overnight, Norman became the Great White Shark. And his personal publicity machine was only too keen to jump on the commercial possibilities they saw and to keep the image alive. A stunt in 1990 when the golfing Great White Shark went cage-diving off the South Australian coast to get close-up and friendly with some of his namesakes was okay; that was just public relations, lapped up by golf followers and golf writers around the world. But the next day, Norman went out game-fishing and actually latched on to a great white. That was serious, and led to a furore that started in Australia and involved Norman in what became a worldwide controversy.

It started in the week leading up to Monday, 5 February in 1990. Norman had been filming a documentary for the American ABC network, part of which involved going down in a shark cage to get close to the beasts whose name he bears. Once the filming was finished, however, it seems somebody suggested a bit of big-game fishing would be a good idea. Well, it may have seemed like a good idea at the time, a bit of relaxation on the water with the ever-present possibility of hooking up on a big fish, but as with so many good ideas at the time ... it wasn't. The Great White Shark left in his wake a dead great white and a raging battle about the morality and ethics of killing the animals for no gain other than a trophy to hang over the fireplace in a multi-million dollar Florida hideaway.

As the war of words continued, it spread to take in the whole issue of the techniques used in game-fishing. The local fishermen of Port Lincoln, state and local government officials and the television production company filming the documentary about Norman all ducked for cover. They wanted desperately to distance themselves from his fishing trip, saying it was purely a private venture. The producer of the ABC documentary, Ms Narelle Barsby, even went so far as to say she and her production team did not support and did not film the killing of sharks. That was just one slap in the face for Norman, but more were to come.

The shark in question was a 488-kilogram male great white, which Norman caught off Langton Island, about 30 kilometres north-west of Port Lincoln.

After landing it on Port Lincoln quayside just before midnight, Norman said he had intended only to tag his victim and return it to the sea. But he said the shark had twisted itself around the line in its fight for freedom, become tangled and had died before it could be hauled aboard the boat to be tagged and then set free. Despite those professed good intentions, a physically worn and tired Norman couldn't hide his glee at catching the huge fish.

And before the tidal wave of controversy washed over him, Norman joyously related how he did battle with another much larger fish. He told how he had spent four hours on the end of a rod in a 'one-on-one fight' with a second, larger shark which he believed could have been a world-record catch. But as night descended, the shark snapped the 24-kilogram line Norman was using to qualify for the record. Norman was on board a 14-metre game-fishing boat *Top Gun*, owned by Adelaide businessman Sam Rocatti. Everyone involved in the brewing controversy was glad the boat at the centre of the issue was owned by an out-of-towner, especially the Port Lincoln locals, who took every chance to distance themselves from involvement.

Even the marketing manager for Lincoln Cove, Mr Ian Nightingale, who organized accommodation for Norman and provided a support vessel, the *Dangerous Reef Explorer*, said he and Lincoln Cove were not directly involved. Bruce Bennett, the manager of Sea Charter, which carried out the berleying for the trip from another boat, said it was a 'purely commercial arrangement' and his personal feelings about killing sharks were 'quite mixed'. Sounds like a case of 'business is business'. Eventually, well after Norman had packed his bags, jumped on his jet and flown the coop, the argument settled down to the use of berley.

Berleying is the practice of spreading fish and animal remains, including blood, leaving a trail in the ocean currents behind a boat. The target fish discover the trail and follow it towards the boat, where they are presented with the baited hooks. It is simply a system used to attract more fish to the area into which the fishermen are casting their lines, and is not used exclusively for big game expeditions. Berleying can be used effectively in lakes, rivers, inlets and even when fishing the surf from an ocean beach. But somehow, when it is used in the hunt for big game fish, the practice seems a little like entrapment in legal terms. It smacks of bad sportsmanship.

In the Great White Shark (Greg Norman) furore, the use of berley to attract the sharks was described as 'immoral' by local boat charterers because of the danger to nearby seal colonies and visitors who swim among them. The owner of the Tumby Bay-based charter boat, *Sea Jade*, Mr Chris Elliott, said berleying should be banned around the Sir Joseph Banks group of islands, which includes Langton Island, because of the danger to the seals. He said he thought game fishermen might be using the area because berleying was now banned at nearby Dangerous Reef.

'We know there are sometimes sharks out there, we just don't want more attracted to the area and perhaps learning that food comes from boats.' His wife, Mrs Julie Elliott, said sightings of sharks were rare among the Sir Joseph Banks islands but the subject was an emotive one after Port Lincoln mother, Mrs Shirley Ann Durdin, was taken by a shark at Wiseman's Beach in March, 1985 (see page 155).

As the battle raged, Norman was given another telling-off by marine scientist, Dr Ian Gordon, who was a resident researcher at the Manly Underwater World in Sydney. He said he doubted the shark had drowned as a result of being tangled in the wire trace and believed measures could have been taken to save it. He added scathingly that the Great White's (Norman's) great white had been sacrificed for the sake of publicity. As it happened, Jacques Cousteau, the famous French underwater explorer, was in Australia at the time to receive an award, and he joined the party as well. He said Norman should apologize for having killed the shark. Another well-known and highly respected Australian expert, Valerie Taylor, who worked as a technical adviser on the movie blockbuster, *Jaws*, also protested.

'He calls himself the 'Great White Shark', and here he is killing the creature that he would symbolize,' she said scathingly. As for the shark? It was snap frozen and shipped to the United States for stuffing and mounting before taking up residence at Norman's Florida home.

Titbits & Trivia

Quick Bites

by John Pinkney

Hush! He Hears your Heartbeat!

The shark, like humans and other animals, has the five basic senses – sight, smell, hearing, touch and taste. But in addition it's equipped with devastatingly effective sixth and seventh senses which enable it to detect faint movements in the water, metres away – and to 'listen in' on the internal digestive rumblings, muscle movements and heartbeats of potential prey.

Best-understood of these bonus senses is *electroreception,* which picks up electrical fields emitted by fish, water animals such as seals – and human swimmers. Electroreceptors (known as 'ampullae of Lorenzini') can be found behind the shark's eyes and in its snout and lips. The receptors link to jelly-filled tubes which connect with pores on the skin.

Many marine creatures burrow beneath the sand when a shark lashes lazily into view – but it can be a pointless precaution. If the predator's electroreceptors don't find it, the *hair-cell sensors* will. These tiny super-receivers nestle inside blind skin pockets, covering the shark's hide. They make the shark a swimming radio-station, ready to pick up the faintest indication of life.

The ferocious fish's conventional senses shouldn't be underestimated, either. Animals, like dogs, which emit a strong odour both in and out of the water, stand little chance when a shark is sniffing about. A human swimmer nursing a grazed knee or cut finger can be in danger too.

A shark can smell one part of blood in 10 billion parts of water – the equivalent of detecting a baby's tear shed in an Olympic swimming pool. Sharks can see in colour – and can detect shapes in water which a human would perceive only as pitch-blackness.

Fangs Galore

A seemingly inexhaustible supply of teeth grow in the shark's jaws. These ultra-efficient, meat-shredding molars are set in layered rows in the gums. If a tooth drops out, as a result of age or during a particularly violent feeding frenzy, a tooth from another layer takes its place. The average shark is likely to shed up to *50,000* teeth in its lifetime.

This dental extravagance is one reason why prehistoric shark teeth are the most commonly found fossils.

Shy About their Age

On average a shark takes only *seven days* to grow a new molar. The shark's high-speed tooth turnover makes life tough for scientists studying the species. Researchers can determine the ages of most creatures by studying their teeth. But this is impossible with sharks, so their precise lifespan can only be guessed at … except in rare cases where the vertebrae, treelike, add an annual ring of growth.

Gory Signatures

Shark attack victims can seldom say what species it was that attacked them. However, marine experts may often find out by analyzing toothmarks left in the wounds. The grey nurse, the bull shark and the tiger shark for example, all have quite distinctively-shaped fangs ... teeth that can leave unmistakable IDs (*ident*ification marks) in human flesh.

The Speedy – and the Slow

Great whites and bronze whalers are among the fastest swimmers in the sea – hurtling forward, when prey is involved, at up to 50 kilometres per hour. Whales and dolphins stand little chance against them. Fast sharks keep their bodies stiff, like torpedoes – and move constantly, even when 'resting', to keep water-borne oxygen streaming past their gills. But the oceans are filled, too, with slower, more laid-back sharks which use less energy and less oxygen. They like to take long rests between plodding swims.

They're not only Fast – They Fast!

Sharks are not necessarily the bottomless-bellied eating machines you see in movies. The average shark can go six weeks without eating – and emerge from the ordeal as fit as a trout. The record for one of these big fish-fasts was set by a 'swell-shark' in a Florida aquarium. Scientists attested that it had eaten no food for *15 months*.

Mystery of the Missing Skeleton

Sharks belong to the fish family. But unlike most fish they have no internal skeleton – relying instead on an external armour of *cartilage*. Sandpaper-rough, this covering is stippled with tooth-like scales called *denticles*. Cartilage is softer and less firm than bone – and may, to a casual observer, look like an evolutionary weakness. But over the aeons, cartilaginous fish have grown larger and stronger than their bony cousins.

The whale shark – at up to 14 metres the biggest fish of all – wears a cartilage coat. And many smaller sharks are powerful enough to hunt and rip to pieces fish of greater size, like tuna.

The Sickening Stare

The shark has upper and lower eyelids. But it never blinks.

Some species have a membrane that slides down to protect the eyes. The great white uses a different method – rolling its eyes upward so that only the whites are visible.

Nurses from Hell

The grey nurse is one of Australia's most feared sharks – but no-one seems sure how its family, the *nurse* sharks, got their name. One theory is that they're plain grey or brown, like uniformed hospital nurses. Another is that some suck their food from the seabed with a gurgling noise that sounds like a suckling foal or poddy-calf.

Minority Report

Sharks comprise only around *one per cent* of the fish that swarm in our planet's seas. But they've been there longer: an estimated 400 million years. During that cosmic blink of time, the *elasmobranchs* (scientific term for sharks and their cousins, the rays) have developed killer-application adaptations that have made them in some senses, masters of the sea.

Sharks are older than dinosaurs – and demonstrably more efficient.

Australia: World's Shark Capital

Australia enjoys the distinction of having almost *half* the world's shark species (165 out of 340) swimming in its seas and rivers. Aussie sharks range in size from the puny pygmy (27 centimetres long) to the massive whale shark (at 12+ metres long, the biggest fish on earth).

Brainless? Don't Bank on It!

Movies like *Jaws* depict the shark as a mindless killing machine – a blindly insatiable hunger-thing driven only by the smell of prey. But in the last 20 years researchers in aquariums and wild testing-grounds have raised doubts about this prejudice. Their experiments show that sharks can use their moderately-sized brains to recognize patterns and remember stimuli.

Some observers report that sharks have complex behaviour patterns we are only slowly beginning to understand – and sophisticated experiments are showing sharks are capable of learning. Already sharks have proved they can perform such tasks as ringing a bell to get a meal.

And in the wild, the creatures repeatedly show they're capable of much more than mere pouncing.

One example is the gigantic whale sharks which, every autumn, suddenly appear off Western Australia's Ningaloo Reef. Their visit coincides with the spawning of coral and other reef creatures – which in turn generates a vast increase in plankton, the whale shark's staple diet.

Bedroom Secrets: Dating and Mating

Between the pelvic fins, the male shark sports a pair of claspers. When he meets a female he fancies, he inserts one of these organs into her cloaca and transfers sperm. Most matings of this kind occur on the sea floor – but some species swim side by side while generating new life.

A few species (such as the Port Jackson shark) lay spiral-shelled eggs, often washed up on our southern beaches. But other sharks give birth to living young – the embryo having been nourished in the yolk sac and its development completed in the uterus.

Murder in the Maternity Ward

Savagery dominates the birth process in some shark species. The Australian grey nurse shark produces particularly ruthless offspring. The two first-hatched young eat the others – with the result that only two strong pups survive.

Having emerged upside-down and tail-first, shark pups

immediately right themselves and start swimming. In the pitiless ocean, the slow are swallowed.

Move Aside, Mum!

Baby sharks spend no time at all with their mothers. From the instant of birth or hatching they swim and forage independently. However, like the young of humans and other mammals, they grow very slowly, taking years to achieve maturity and the ability to reproduce. Scientists believe sharks keep growing until they die.

Shocks: Inside a Shark's Stomach

During the 1940s a 3.5-metre whaler shark caught near Sydney was found to have an astonishing variety of undigested food in its stomach.

The creature had gobbled:

- eight legs of mutton
- half a ham
- a dog's hindquarters
- 135 kilograms of horsemeat
- a ship's scraper
- and to soak it all up, a piece of sacking

At that time no law existed to prevent abattoirs dumping their rubbish in the sea. The stomach-churning discovery lent further fuel to the old belief that sharks will eat anything that gets in their way. But that's a myth. Although they can be useful scavengers, especially in a mass feeding frenzy, most sharks are quite particular about what they'll consume.

They seem able also to *delay digestion* of their food. A large tiger shark, which died at Sydney's Taronga Zoo after a month's captivity, was found to have two dolphins in its stomach – almost perfectly preserved.

A Diet to Die for

Sharks swallow a large variety of foods. The Port Jackson shark is partial to *sea urchins,* which it crushes with its flat teeth – a habit that often stains the jaws purple. The major maulers prefer stronger meat. The great white and the bull shark will chomp on anything that moves, from seals and dogs to people and fellow sharks.

And when they're peckish they can process food quickly. In one Queensland case a large shark was killed while a smaller shark's tail was still protruding from its mouth. When the victim was sawn clear of its attacker's jaws, the head was already a shapeless mass – digested beyond recognition.

Ringleaders and Riff-Raff

Like birds, sharks have a pronounced pecking – or chomping – order. Although normally solitary creatures, they'll quickly adopt dominance patterns when they encounter fellow-elasmobranchs.

Silvertip sharks off Papua New Guinea's coast are particularly rough on their reef-dwelling cousins – butting and snapping whenever food is at stake. Scientists have observed male bonnethead sharks adopt a threatening 'hunch' posture towards intruders. They'll unchivalrously bite and bump their own females, to ensure the chaps keep the pick of the feast to themselves.

Who are the Killers – Them or Us?

Humans kill millions of the world's sharks annually – to supply the food, manufacturing and medical industries. In an average year, sharks worldwide will kill fewer than ten people.

Aussie Seas are Deadliest

Sharks killed more people in Australia in 2000 than anywhere else on Earth. Worldwide, 79 attacks – 10 fatal – were documented. Fiji, Japan, Papua New Guinea, New Caledonia and the United States each reported 1 death; Tanzania suffered 2; and Australia 3.

In the two centuries 1803-2003, 187 Australians have died in shark attacks.

Shark Death Statistics 1803-2003

State	Attacks	Deaths	Last Fatal Attack
New South Wales	227	72	1993: Byron Bay
Queensland	218	70	2003: Gold Coast
Victoria	31	7	1977: Mornington Peninsula
South Australia	43	19	2002: Smoky Bay
Western Australia	56	11	2000: Cottlesloe Beach
Northern Territory	10	3	1938 Bathurst Island
Tasmania	21	5	1993: Tenth Island, Georgetown
Total	606	187	(As of February 2003)

Source: Taronga Zoo and the Australian Shark Attack File

From 1983 to 2003 Australia has recorded 24 shark deaths – an average of 1.2 annually (Queensland, 9; South Australia, 9; New South Wales, 1; Tasmania, 1; Victoria, 0; Western Australia, 4; Nothern Territory, 0).

Beware the Killer Coconut!

To keep things in perspective, falling coconuts kill an average of 150 people annually – 15 times the number of humans killed by sharks.

'Bite-and-Spit': The Ugliest Death of All

Some shark species have a horrifying habit of lunging at a victim (occasionally a human) – biting deeply, then moving swiftly away, to wait for the maimed prey to die. This behaviour, say experts, minimizes the predator's risk of being injured in a counter-attack.

Often, when a human is involved, the picky shark may back off for aesthetic reasons (see 'Ugh! They Hate the Taste of Us' on page 226).

Man in the Grey Steel Suit

Academic Steve Wilson of the University of Western Australia was bitten by sharks so often (one arm-wound needed 28 stitches) that he took counter-measures. He upgraded his undersea wardrobe to a $5,000 chain-mail 'over-garment' to cover his wetsuit. 'That spread the pressure from the points of the shark's teeth right across my body – reducing it to something like a dog bite,' Steve recalled.

'Before I wore the chain-mail I'd several times seen my hand disappear into a shark's mouth and thought, Oh, no, I've lost it. But the shark always spat it out again.'

Ugh! They Hate the Taste of Us!

Only 32 shark species are known to have attacked humans. Most attacks are accidents. When a shark swims into the same warm-water shallows as a person it may mistake him, or her, for natural prey. The shark speeds in for the kill – but usually abandons the attack after the first bite. They just don't like the way we taste.

Shark Slang

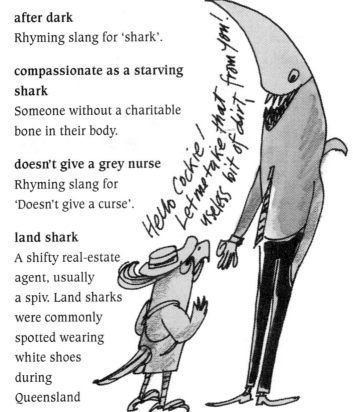

The importance of the shark in the Australian psyche is reflected in the frequency it crops up in our slang. Here are a few examples.

after dark
Rhyming slang for 'shark'.

compassionate as a starving shark
Someone without a charitable bone in their body.

doesn't give a grey nurse
Rhyming slang for 'Doesn't give a curse'.

land shark
A shifty real-estate agent, usually a spiv. Land sharks were commonly spotted wearing white shoes during Queensland

property booms, flogging high-rise jerry-built apartments and mosquito-infested swampland as prime holiday sites.

loan shark
A moneylender or pawnbroker who believes in extortionate interest rates. It has also lately come to refer to the upper echelons of the banking industry for obvious reasons.

lower than shark shit
Someone definitely not to be trusted. One who is sneaky, conniving and dishonest (as in 'lower than a snake's belly').

Noah's Ark/Noah
Rhyming slang for 'shark'.

sea lawyer
Derogatory term, to both lawyers and sharks.

shark bait
See 'swimming with the sharks'.

shark biscuit.
Somebody new to surfing.

swimming with the sharks
Refers to someone who is swimming way further out than anyone else. It can also refer to someone who is in a lot of trouble or about to be in a lot of trouble (as in someone is who 'walking on very thin ice').

white pointers
female sunbathers, topless.

wouldn't shout if a shark bit him
That's the bloke we all know who always seems to miss his turn at the bar. It is the same as describing someone as having short arms and long pockets. In a word – tightfisted.

wouldn't use him/her for shark bait
Used to describe a despicable individual – someone you
wouldn't trust around your wife/husband.

(Cartoons reproduced by permission of Geoff Hocking.)

Shark Dreams

*I*t seems that sharks figure quite strongly in many people's dreams, and there is certainly plenty of pop-psychology about, not to mention pop-psychologists, who are only to happy to interpret the meanings of the role in dreams. Drowning or near-drowning is also a common thread, but more specifically dreams involving sharks do have certain underlying meanings about the waking life of the dreamer.

When it comes to sharks, there's no such thing as a good dream. All the meanings attributed to a shark dream, or perhaps nightmare is a better word, appear to be forebodings of bad events or hard times. And naturally very different meanings apply if the dreamer is the shark rather than the victim.

If you dream about being the shark it may mean you are feeling hard done by or slighted in some way, and want to metaphorically get your teeth into the person responsible. But it may also mean you are not accepting what other people are telling you. Perhaps you feel you are being fed a line of old codswallop at work, at school, at home or socially. After all, sharks are the ravenous ocean scavengers, all sorts of weird and wonderful – and unpalatable – things have been found in their stomachs.

Perhaps you feel people expect you, like the shark, to swallow any old thing that comes your way.

If you are attacked by a shark in your dream, it may mean you believe, consciously or sub-consciously, that someone out there is out to get you. Excluding unfounded paranoia, ask yourself if there is anyone in the circle in which you move who wants to do you harm. You may feel you are going through life surrounded by people who want to rule your life, make all your decisions for you, and in effect just overpower you as a person. Ask yourself if you believe you are surrounded by opportunists who would happily walk all over you for their own benefit.

Then there's the style of the attack to consider:

If you are happily playing in the water and a passing shark launches a surprise attack, are you in reality expecting something unwelcome to arise shortly? It may be something you should be considering, something you know deep down is a possibility, but which you are refusing to acknowledge in your waking hours. *Or did the shark stalk you before attacking?* Did it circle, weaving in and out of your vision, seeming to wait for just the right time to strike? That could be an indication of pressure in real life. Situations are developing around you over which you feel you have no control, and all you can do is wait and watch and be ready for the inevitable assault. Of course, the seemingly inevitable can be changed; in your dream just getting away from the deep water and back to the safety of the shore could well represent getting yourself out of a waking situation. It's time to take stock, to assess your waking position and leave the shark infested waters.

Shark Jokes

Heard this one? We frequently make jokes about the things we fear most – so it's not surprise that there are plenty of shark jokes doing the rounds.

A white pointer and a giant squid come across each other in the middle of the ocean, and naturally a savage fight breaks out. For a while the shark is getting the worst of it, but he eventually prevails and gives the squid a fearful battering.

Taking the giant squid in his mouth, the shark swims towards a reef, where his friend, a loan shark, is hanging out. He swims up to his mate and spits out the barely-live squid and says 'Here's the sick squid I owe you'.

A surfer, who happens to be a confirmed atheist, is way out the back where the biggest waves are, just waiting for the perfect break to come along and give him the ride of his life when he's confronted by the biggest white pointer he's ever seen. He pulls himself up on his board and sits, watching terrified as the great white circles ominously. Then, from 50 metres away, the shark starts its run. Straight at him, coming in like an express train, huge jaws opening to reveal row after row of razor-sharp teeth.

Just as the shark is about to rear out of the water and end his life in one mighty gulp, the surfer calls out, 'Oh God, please help me.'

Instantly, time stops, the sea is calm, the great white is suspended half in the air and the clouds part. A booming voice comes from the heavens and speaks to the surfer. 'You call on me for help, but you're an atheist, and you don't believe in me do you?' God asks.

Stunned, the surfer can only respond: 'Well no, I don't believe in you, but can you make this bloody great shark believe in you?'

'I'll see what I can do,' says God. Within seconds the clouds close over again, the waves start moving, and the surfer hears a strange noise.

He looks around and there's the shark, jaws wide open about to swallow him whole, when it stops mid-plunge and backs off a little. Then it folds its fins in front of its body and says quietly, 'For what we are about to receive, may the Lord make us truly grateful, Amen.'

The lion-tamer, the priest and the lawyer are among the passengers stranded on a deserted island after a shipwreck. It looks as if everybody is going to be on the island for some time, but everything they need for survival is still aboard the ship which is stuck fast on a reef out in the lagoon. The water in the lagoon is teeming with sharks, but the stranded passengers are getting desperate, so the lion tamer announces one morning he will attempt to swim out to the ship.

'I am the mightiest lion tamer in the world,' he announces. 'The sharks do not scare me.' He runs into the water and starts swimming as fast as he can, arms and legs thrashing at the water. He gets to a point 50 metres from the beach, and the castaways are all holding their breath. At one hundred metres from the beach, they begin to think he has a chance when there's a mighty eruption in the water all around him as dozens of sharks close in for the kill.

Days go by and the plight of the stranded group is getting desperate. The priest announces he will attempt the swim the next morning, and goes into the jungle to pray for guidance. In the morning he announces on the beach that he has prayed all night and is confident his faith will prevail over the pack of sharks.

'I have been a truly religious man all my life,' he stated. 'I have led a pure and holy existence and my God will protect me in our hour of need.' With that he disrobed and took calmly to the water, swimming with long powerful strokes towards the ship. At 50 metres out from shore, the crowd on the beach are again holding their breath. At 100 metres, the priest is still swimming confidently towards the wreck. At 150 metres, it looks as if the priest will make it when suddenly there's a terrible turmoil in the water and he disappears as well.

More days go by until there is no food left, and only a bucket of water. The lawyer steps forward and quietly announces he will attempt the swim. The following morning he strides into the water and makes for the wreck. At 50 metres from shore, he turns and waves at the crowd of onlookers. At 100 metres, the crowd is back to holding its breath. Then the lawyer passes the 150-metre mark with no sign of trouble. He reaches the wreck and clambers aboard, putting together as many supplies as he can tow behind him on the swim back.

When he gets back into the water and starts swimming towards shore he has an escort of dozens of sharks, guiding him through the breakers and towards the beach. As he steps onto the sand dozens of voices cry out: 'Why didn't the sharks attack and eat you?'

'Professional courtesy' said the lawyer.

Two blokes were out fishing in a small dinghy one day and a freak wave turned their boat over. Watching about 100 metres away were two sharks, and one shark says to the other: 'There's lunch. I'll go first and come back, then you can go.'

'Okay,' says the second shark as he watches his mate heading straight for one of the floundering fishermen and swallow him whole.

'Beautiful,' call outs the first shark. 'I'll wait here and you go get the other one.' With that the second shark heads off after the other bloke. Twenty metres away ... ten metres away and jaws wide open … five metres … three – then all of a sudden he does a U-turn and comes back.

'What happened?' asks the first shark. 'You had him all lined up.'

'I know,' said the second shark glumly, 'and I was about to take him whole when I spotted what was on his T-shirt. It said 'Collingwood Premiers for 2004' and there was no bloody way I was swallowing that.'

(Cartoons reproduced courtesy Geoff Hocking)

Things to Do with a Dead Shark

Apart from the Friday bag of chips and a bit of flake, or a bowl of shark fin soup at your favourite Asian eatery, there's a startling array of other shark by-products. Traditional Chinese medicine uses skin, bile, embryos, ovaries, cartilage, fins, brain, flesh and liver oil from sharks. More and more sharkskin is being used for ornamental purposes, leather and shagreen, which is a sort of rough untanned leather. Shagreen is also a sandpaper-like abrasive made from the skin of certain species.

Shark liver oil – now there's a product to make anyone with memories of cod liver oil wince, but what useful stuff it is. It's used as a lubricant, a leather-tanning agent, vitamin A concentrate and a treatment for waterproofing timber. Occasionally, an old-timer who spends a lot of time fishing will tell you it's good to soak your undies in it to protect against the cold, but that's in the 'believe-it-or-not-category'.

The liver oil from some sharks is rich in squalene, which we turn into lubricants, anti-bacterial agents, medicine and cosmetics. Even the cartilage which sharks have instead of a skeleton is useful. It's used in the manufacture of artificial skin for burns victims, covering damaged tissue while the victim's own skin repairs itself underneath. The cartilage is even used as a component of some eye drops, and researchers have been testing the possibility it may be an effective treatment for arthritis and some cancers. The jury is still out on the cancer side, but arthritis is looking good, at least in the lab.

Australia is one of the world's biggest producers of shark cartilage, and we also extract and refine shark liver oil, mostly for export. Of course there are the far more pedestrian uses for bits and pieces of the old 'Noah's Ark', too. The glue factory or the fertiliser works may well be the fate of sharks which don't have fish-market quality flesh. They may even be converted to farm animal meal or simply chopped up as bait.

Once everything else is used we're left pretty much with jaws and teeth, and if the jaws are big enough they could well end up mounted on a board on some tourist's wall at home. As for the teeth, well, the most likely end-use for them is being worn on a leather thong around another tourist's neck because the shonky bloke at the flea market swore that shark's teeth are a traditional native love amulet, guaranteed to get you into the arms of the one you fancy.

In the Northern Territory, however, one family, pardon the pun, made a bit of a killing out of the Aussie fascination with sharks. They went to a garage sale, and sight-unseen purchased a box of cast-off Barbie dolls. When they got home they found a couple of the dolls were damaged: one had its feet and hands chewed and another had an arm and a leg missing. They held their own garage sale a little later, and the Barbie with chewed hands and feet became 'Pit-Bull Barbie'. The one with one arm and one leg missing, naturally, became 'Shark Attack Barbie'.

Waste Not, Want Not

Human predators leave no scrap of the shark unused.

- The meat becomes fertiliser – when it is'nt being battered and served with potato cakes
- The eyes are used in corneal transplants
- The blood can be found in a bewildering variety of remedies – prescribed and 'natural'
- The cartilage is an ingredient in burns treatments
- The liver provides squalene for cosmetics ... oil rich in Vitamin A ... industrial and vehicle lubricants ... garden sprays ... and ingredients for paints
- The fins support a vast Asian soup industry
- The skin makes abrasives, handbags and shoes
- The plentiful teeth are transformed into jewellery and weapons.

Even if you're a strict vegetarian you will – probably unwittingly – use several shark-based products today.

Getting Even

While some sharks may make a meal of some of us, the scales are heavily tipped in human favour. In some parts of the world the skin, heart, stomach, intestine, liver, gills and eggs are gobbled up with relish. Surprisingly, just about every cuisine style has come up with something useful to do with sharks.

Shark Fin Soup is probably the most widely known and we have a recipe for it in this section. But recently the traditional Chinese dish has been coming under close scrutiny. The international environmental watchdog, Wild Aid, has reported that shark fins from Hong Kong, which are sold in street markets throughout Asia, pose a serious health risk. In fact, according to Wild Aid, the sharks pose more of a risk to human life dead than they do alive. The organization said in a report that shark fins sold in restaurants and markets throughout Asia, and the rest of the world contained dangerous levels of mercury. Levels of the poisonous heavy metal found in shark fins for sale in Thailand were 42 times more than safe limits for humans.

Wild Aid said there were only about 25 shark attacks on humans recorded worldwide each year, which by comparison makes dead sharks more dangerous to human health than live ones. But first and foremost, at least in Australia, the most widespread method of turning the 'Shark Bites Man' story into a 'Man Bites Shark' story is the bit of grilled or battered and deep-fried flake. Here are some samples, starting off with one of the basics.

Beer Batter

This recipe makes about two cups of batter, enough for several nice fresh fillets. Just multiply the ingredients depending on how much fish you have.

You will need

1 dozen cans of your favourite brew
1 egg
1 cup plain flour
a good pinch of salt

Method

Drink one of the beers just to get in the mood, then beat the egg in a bowl and add one cup of beer, beating until smooth. Add flour and salt and keep beating until smooth. Allow batter to sit for 30 minutes before using. Lightly flour your fish before dipping in the batter and submerge in hot oil. Cook until pale golden brown. Ask a friend around to finish off the rest of the beers over a fine plate of flake.

Grilled Shark

Quick and snappy!

You will need

1 fillet of shark per person
1 large slice of apple per fillet
canola oil
salt and pepper
your choice of spicy chutney

Method

Get fairly thick fillets, one per person, and with a sharp knife slice along the side to make a pocket. Insert slice of apple in pocket and oil the fish to keep it from sticking. Season fish with a little salt and pepper, or whatever seasoning you prefer. Grill over moderate coals or moderate gas barbie for a few minutes per side until cooked as desired. Serve with your choice of chutney or sauce.

Shark Fin Soup

Now we're getting a little more complicated, but everyone should try this Chinese classic at last once in a lifetime.

You will need

500 g shark fin
6 cups water
6 slices of fresh ginger (each about the size of a $2 coin)

1 spring onion cut in 5-cm lengths and crushed
125 g ham
125 g chicken
60 g lean pork
3 dried mushrooms
125 g bamboo shoots
2 tbs minced ginger
2 tbs minced spring onion
1½ tsp salt
3 tbs soy sauce
¼ cup dry white wine
4 tbs extra wine
1 egg white, lightly beaten
3 tbs cooking oil
5 cups chicken stock
½ tsp sesame oil
4 tbs cornflour
½ cup water
small saucepan or steamer and a frypan

Method

Bring the wine and three cups of water to the boil. Add three of the ginger slices, half the cut spring onion and the shark fin. Bring to the boil again and lower heat to simmer slowly for 20 minutes. Drain, and discard cooking water, ginger and onion. Repeat with new water and the rest of the ginger and onion.

Mince the ham. Soak the mushrooms in hot water for 20 minutes; steam briefly in a small saucepan or steamer and shred. Mince the bamboo shoot, the remaining fresh ginger and the chicken. Marinate the chicken in one tablespoon of wine, the juice of the minced ginger, half the egg white and half a teaspoon of cornflour for ten minutes.

Mince the pork and marinate it in one tablespoon soy sauce and one tablespoon wine. Heat one tablespoon of oil over medium heat in a small frypan. Cook the pork for one or two minutes until just done and set aside.

Heat the other tablespoon of oil and cook the chicken. Heat a soup pot with the last tablespoon of oil, two tablespoons of wine and five cups of chicken sock. Add shark fin and simmer for one hour.

Add the rest of the ingredients, except the cornflour, and simmer for another ten minutes. Taste and season. Mix the cornflour with half a cup of water and stir in. Boil one or two minutes to thicken.

Asian Shark Steak

This sounds delicious and dead easy as well. This recipe is enough for four serves.

You will need
4 shark steaks cut 2-3 cms thick
¼ cup soy sauce
1 tbs sesame oil
1 tbs olive oil
2 tbs lemon juice
¼ tsp ground ginger

1 clove garlic, minced
1 tbs mustard of your choice
½ tbs sugar

Method

Mix all ingredients except shark steaks and pour mixture over the steaks in a shallow baking dish. Marinade for about one hour, turning occasionally. Pour off excess marinade and put aside. Put marinated steaks on the barbie, cooking four or five minutes per side and brush on extra marinade when turning.

Shark Teriyaki

Another barbecue recipe. Very quick and easy.

You will need

Shark steaks, one per person
1 tbs teriyaki sauce
1 tbs honey
1 tbs lemon juice
3 tbs melted margarine
1 minced garlic clove
1 tbs sesame seeds

Method

Put fish in a hinged fish-cooker, preferably oiled to prevent sticking. Combine everything else and baste fish. Cook on a moderately hot barbecue for 4 or 5 minutes, baste again and turn and cook other side for another 4 or 5 minutes.

Citrus Marinated Shark

Something with a bit of Caribbean magic for two people who want to zing.

You will need

2 shark steaks (about 250 g each)
juice of 3 limes
juice of 3 lemons
½ cup coconut cream
60 ml tequila
3 tbs chopped spring onions
2 tbs finely chopped red pepper
2 tbs finely chopped yellow pepper
2 finely chopped jalapeno chilies
salt and ground black pepper to taste
olive oil

Method

Mix everything together except for the shark steaks and olive oil. Place the fish in a casserole dish and pour the marinade over the top. Refrigerate for 24 hours. Heat the olive oil in a pan and remove the shark from the marinade. Sear fish for 2 minutes per side, remove from pan and slice. Place on a plate around a mound of salad and garnish with something green.

Baby Shark Fry

Quick and simple, with a touch of the Mediterranean.

You will need

4 good size shark fillets (about 250 g each)
¼ cup finely chopped tomato
¼ cup of minced onion
corn oil
2 tbs flour
1 beaten egg

Method

Fry the tomato and onion in 1 tablespoon of oil for a few minutes to make the simple sauce. In another frypan heat 3 tablespoons of oil to moderately hot. Dip the shark steaks in the flour and then coat them with the beaten egg. Brown in the oil, approximately 3 minutes per side. Allow to drain briefly on a paper towel and serve warm, pouring the sauce over the fish.

Cape Shark Kebabs

Something very different for next summer around the swimming pool.

You will need

1 kg thickish shark fillets
¼ cup olive oil
½ cup dry white wine
3 tbs lemon juice
1 tsp fresh or dried dill
½ tsp chervil
2 red or green peppers
cherry tomatoes
paprika
lemon wedges for garnish

Method

Cut shark into 2.5-cm cubes, rinse with water and pat dry. Prepare marinade by mixing olive oil, white wine, lemon juice, dill and chervil in a dish large enough to hold all the fish. Place fish in marinade and put in refrigerator for an hour.

Thread fish cubes on a skewer, alternating with slices of pepper and cherry tomatoes. Sprinkle kebabs with paprika and barbecue until done, basting frequently with marinade. Serve with lemon wedges and rice or pasta. Mushrooms, squash or zucchini can be used as well as peppers and cherry tomatoes.

Shark Vindaloo

If the sharks think they can give us curry in the water, let's see how they cope with getting curried.

You will need

900 g of small shark steaks
3 tbs sunflower oil
1 chopped onion
2 roughly chopped tomatoes
4 tbs vindaloo curry paste
300 ml water
8 small green chilies
white wine vinegar to taste
salt

Method

Season the shark steaks with salt. Heat the oil in a large, deep frypan, add the onion and fry until browned. Add the tomatoes and cook until they form a rich golden paste. Stir in the vindaloo paste and fry gently for five minutes, stirring until the mixture has slightly caramelized. Pour in the water and simmer for ten minutes, stirring occasionally.

Slit the green chilies lengthwise and scrape out the seeds, leaving the chilies whole. Add the shark steaks and the chilies to the sauce and simmer for ten minutes, carefully turning the steaks halfway through. Add vinegar and salt to taste and serve on a bed of rice.

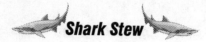

Shark Stew

Forget the beef and lamb. Try this for a hearty winter warmer.

You will need

1 kg of shark, preferably cut into strips about 8 x 2 cm
2 cups celery pieces
2 chopped medium onions
3 tbs water
250 g stewed and seasoned tomatoes
½ cup chopped coriander
cooked rice
salsa
coriander leaves
yoghurt or sour cream
lime wedges
salt and pepper

Method

In a large pot combine celery, onions and water. Put on a medium/high heat and stir often until the water evaporates and vegetables start to stick and brown slightly. Stir in tomatoes and their liquid along with chopped coriander. Bring to the boil and push fish pieces down into the liquid. Cover and simmer on low heat until the fish is opaque (about 20 minutes).

Ladle the stew into wide bowls, serve with cooked rice, salsa, coriander leaves, yoghurt, lime wedges and salt and pepper to taste.

Requin au Four

That's right, even the French want to get a bit of their own back. By the way, the name of this dish is French for 'Baked Shark'.

You will need

500 g of shark fillets (vary to suit numbers)
1 lemon
1 tbs olive oil
salt and pepper
thyme
salt and pepper

Method

Pre-heat oven to 180°C. Slice the shark into pieces and rub oil on each piece. Lightly sprinkle the salt, pepper and herbs over the fish. Squeeze the lemon and pour juice over the meat. Cook for 45 minutes or until the fish is white and tender. Serve with a side plate of sautéed vegetables and béarnaise sauce.

Shark Fin Omelette

Here's a top-tasting variation on the brekky bacon and eggs.

You will need

½ cup died shark fin, soaked and shredded
6 eggs (hen, not shark)
¼ cup smoked ham
½ cup bamboo shoots
2 tbs cooking oil
¼ tsp salt

Method

Beat the eggs and cut the ham and bamboo shoots into slivers. Heat the oil, add salt and then stir-fry the bamboo shoots for one minute. Add shark fin and stir-fry gently to heat through then add ham and stir-fry until heated. Add the beaten eggs and cook as usual for an omelette.

Shark Hors d'Oeuvres

And finally, something from the southern states of the United States with a touch of Creole about it.

You will need

1 kg shark meat cut into 5-cm chunks
¼ cup lemon or lime juice
2 cloves of garlic, crushed
1 cup seasoned flour (your own choice of seasoning)
1 cup breadcrumbs
tartar sauce or a creole mustard
¼ cup dry white wine
salt and pepper to taste
2 beaten eggs
vegetable oil

Method

Mix the lemon juice, wine and garlic. Pour over the shark chunks and marinate in refrigerator for at least an hour. Dip each chunk of fish into the seasoned flour, sprinkle with salt and pepper, then coat with the beaten egg and breadcrumbs. Heat the oil and deep-fry fish until golden brown. Drain on paper towels then serve with creole mustard or tartar sauce.

Acknowledgements

*T*his author and the publisher express their thanks to the following people and organizations for permission to reproduce their material in this book:

- Bill Hitchings and The Herald and Weekly Times ('Death from the Deep', page 61)

- The *Adelaide Advertiser* and The Herald and Weekly Times (Editorial, 1 July 1998, page 74)

- John Pinkney (Beaurepaire, Chalmers: The Coogee Tragedy, page 91; 'Shark Claims Champion Bowler', page 99; 'The Case for Conserving Sharks, page 159; 'Should Sharknets Stay?', page 168; 'Quick Bites', page 216; and various other written contributions throughout the book)

- Peter Coster and The Herald and Weekly Times ('Big Ben Strikes Terror Under the Sea', page 113)

- Peter Hackett and The Herald and Weekly Times ('Two Divers who Survived a Brush with White Death, page 127)

- Geoff Hocking (cartoons on pages 227-238)

- Lee Krutop (drawings on pages 18-29)

The Author and the Publisher also gratefully acknowledge the support and information provided by the following organizations: *Adelaide Advertiser*, Melbourne *Herald Sun*, The Herald and Weekly Times, Taronga Zoo, Australian Shark Attack File, Behind the News Poll, CSIRO, and the *Biological Conservation Journal*. Thanks is also extended to the many other people and organizations who provided research and general advice and helped to make this book possible.